Ion Exchange

ISBN 91 970490-3-4

Contents

1. Introduction

Adsorption chromatography depends upon on interactions of different types between solute molecules and ligands immobilized on a chromatography matrix. The first type of interaction to be successfully employed for the separation of macromolecules was that between charged solute molecules and oppositely charged moieties covalently linked to a chromatography matrix. The technique of ion exchange chromatography is based on this interaction.

Today ion exchange is the most frequently used chromatographic technique for the separation and purification of proteins, polypeptides, nucleic acids, polynucleotides and other charged biomolecules, being included in approximately 75% of separation schemes (1).

The reasons for the success of ion exchange are its widespread applicability, its high resolving power, its high capacity and the simplicity and controllability of the method.

This handbook is designed as an introduction to the principles of ion exchange chromatography and as a practical guide to the use of the media available from Pharmacia LKB Biotechnology. The handbook is illustrated with examples of the different types of biological molecules which have been separated using ion exchange chromatography and the different ways the technique can be used. For information on specific separations, the reader is recommended to consult the original literature.

2. Ion exchange chromatography

The theory of ion exchange

Separation in ion exchange chromatography depends upon the reversible adsorption of charged solute molecules to an immobilised ion exchange group of opposite charge. Most ion exchange experiments are performed in five main stages. These steps are illustrated schematically below.

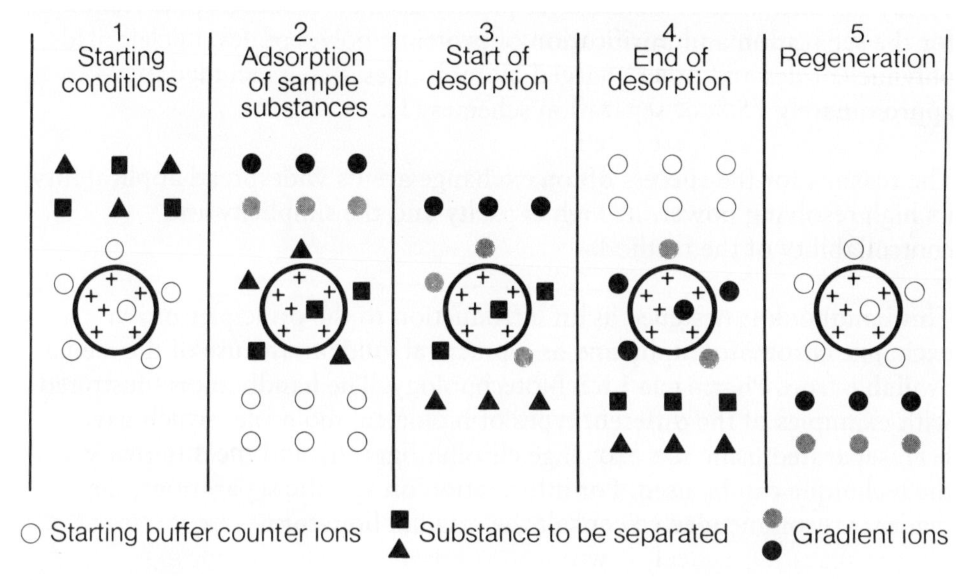

Fig.1. The principles of ion exchange chromatography (salt gradient elution).

The first stage is equilibration in which the ion exchanger is brought to a starting state, in terms of pH and ionic strength, which allows the binding of the desired solute molecules. The exchanger groups are associated at this time with exchangeable counter-ions (usually simple anions or cations, such as chloride or sodium).

The second stage is sample application and adsorption in which solute molecules carrying the appropriate charge displace counter ions and bind reversibly to the gel. Unbound substances can be washed out from the exchanger bed using starting buffer.

In the third stage, substances are removed from the column by changing to elution conditions unfavourable for ionic bonding of the solute molecules.

This normally involves increasing the ionic strength of the eluting buffer or changing its pH. In Figure 1 desorption is achieved by the introduction of an increasing salt concentration gradient and solute molecules are released from the column in the order of their strengths of binding, the most weakly bound substances being eluted first.

The fourth and fifth stages are the removal from the column of substances not eluted under the previous experimental conditions and re-equilibration at the starting conditions for the next purification.

Separation is obtained since different substances have different degrees of interaction with the ion exchanger due to differences in their charges and charge densities. These interactions can be controlled by varying conditions such as ionic strength and pH. The differences in charge properties of biological compounds are often considerable, and since ion exchange chromatography is capable of separating species with very minor differences in properties, e.g. two proteins differing by only one charged amino acid, it is a very powerful separation technique.

In ion exchange chromatography one can choose whether to bind the substances of interest and allow the contaminants to pass through the column, or to bind the contaminants and allow the substance of interest to pass through. Generally, the first method is more useful since it allows a greater degree of fractionation and concentrates the substances of interest.

The conditions under which substances are bound (or free) are discussed in detail in the sections dealing with choice of experimental conditions. In addition to the ion exchange effect, other types of binding may occur. These effects are small and are mainly due to van der Waals forces and non-polar interactions.

Ion exchange separations may be carried out in a column or by a batch procedure. Both methodologies are performed using the definite stages of equilibration, sample adsorption etc. described previously.

The matrix

An ion exchanger consists of an insoluble porous matrix to which charged groups have been covalently bound. The charged groups are associated with mobile counter-ions. These counter-ions can be reversibly exchanged with other ions of the same charge without altering the matrix.

It is possible to have both positively and negatively charged exchangers (Fig. 2). Positively charged exchangers have negatively charged counter-ions (anions) available for exchange and so are termed anion exchangers. Negatively charged exchangers have positively charged counter-ions (cations) and are termed cation exchangers.

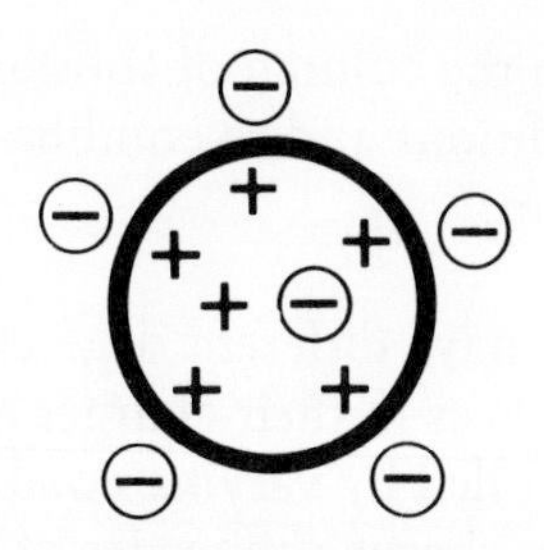

ANION exchanger with exchangeable counter ions

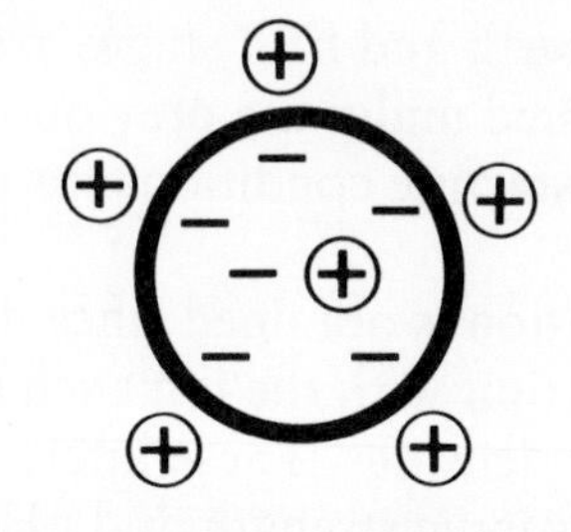

CATION exchanger with exchangeable counter ions

Fig. 2. Ion exchanger types.

The matrix may be based on inorganic compounds, synthetic resins, polysaccharides etc. The characteristics of the matrix determine its chromatographic properties such as resolution, capacity and recovery as well as physical properties such as its mechanical strength and flow properties. The nature of the matrix will also affect its behaviour towards biological substances and the maintenance of biological activity.

The first ion exchangers were synthetic resins designed for applications such as demineralization, water treatment, and recovery of ions from wastes. Such ion exchangers consist of hydrophobic polymer matrices highly substituted with ionic groups, and have very high capacities for small ions. Due to their low permeability these matrices have low capacities for proteins and other macromolecules. In addition, the extremely high charge density gives very strong binding and the hydrophobic matrix tends to denature labile biological materials. Thus despite their excellent flow properties and capacities for small ions, these types of ion exchanger are unsuitable for use with biological samples.

The first ion exchangers designed for use with biological substances were the cellulose ion exchangers developed by Peterson and Sober (2). Because of the hydrophilic nature of cellulose, these exchangers had little tendency to denature proteins. Unfortunately, many cellulose ion exchangers had low capacities (otherwise the cellulose became soluble in water) and had poor flow properties due to their irregular shape.

Ion exchangers based on dextran (Sephadex), followed by those based on agarose (Sepharose CL-6B) and cross-linked cellulose (DEAE Sephacel) were the first ion exchange matrices to combine the correct spherical form with high porosity, leading to improved flow properties and high capacities for macromolecules.

Subsequently, developments in gel technology have enabled this macroporosity to be extended to the highly cross linked agarose-based media such as Sepharose Fast Flow and Sepharose High Performance, and the synthetic polymer matrix, MonoBeads. These modern media offer the possibility of fast, high capacity, high resolution ion exchange chromatography at both analytical and preparative scales.

Charged groups

The presence of charged groups is a fundamental property of an ion exchanger. The type of group determines the type and strength of the ion exchanger; their total number and availability determines the capacity. There is a variety of groups which have been chosen for use in ion exchangers (3); some of these are shown in Table 1.

Table 1. Functional groups used on ion exchangers.

Anion exchangers	Functional group
Diethylaminoethyl (DEAE)	$-OCH_2CH_2N^+H(CH_2CH_3)_2$
Quaternary aminoethyl (QAE)	$-OCH_2CH_2N^+(C_2H_5)_2CH_2CH(OH)CH_3$
Quaternary ammonium (Q)	$-CH_2N^+(CH_3)_3$
Cation exchangers	**Functional group**
Carboxymethyl (CM)	$-OCH_2COO^-$
Sulphopropyl (SP)	$-CH_2CH_2CH_2SO_3^-$
Methyl sulphonate (S)	$-CH_2SO_3^-$

Sulphonic and quaternary amino groups are used to form strong ion exchangers; the other groups form weak ion exchangers. The terms strong and weak refer to the extent of the variation of ionization with pH and not the strength of binding. Strong ion exchangers are completely ionized over a wide pH range (see titration curves on page 36) whereas with weak ion exchangers, the degree of dissociation and thus exchange capacity varies much more markedly with pH.

Some properties of strong ion exchangers are:

- Sample loading capacity does not decrease at high or low pH values due to loss of charge from the ion exchanger.
- A very simple mechanism of interaction exists between the ion exchanger and the solute.
- Ion exchange experiments are more controllable since the charge characteristics of the media do not change with changes in pH. This makes strong exchangers ideal for working with data derived from electrophoretic titration curves. (see Chapter 8)

Resolution in ion exchange chromatography

This section discusses the main theoretical parameters which affect the separation in ion exchange chromatography. For more in-depth information the reader is referred to standard works on the subject (4, 5). The result of an ion exchange experiment, as with any other chromatographic separation, is often expressed as the resolution between the peaks of interest. The resolution (Rs) is determined from the chromatogram as shown in Figure 3.

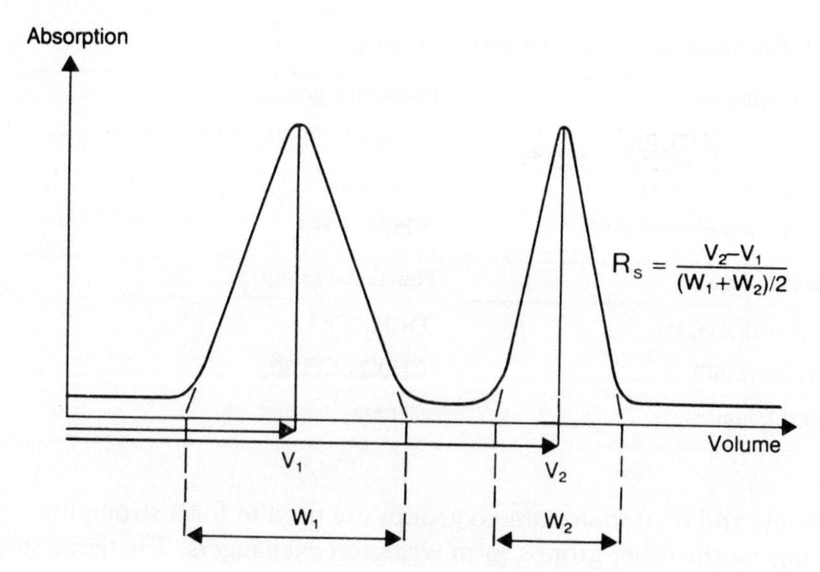

Fig. 3. Determination of the resolution (Rs) between two peaks.

The resolution is defined as the distance between peak maxima compared with the average base width of the two peaks. Elution volumes and peak widths should be measured with the same units to give a dimensionless value to the resolution.

Rs is a measure of the relative separation between two peaks and can be used to determine if further optimization of the chromatographic procedure is necessary. If Rs = 1.0 (Fig. 4) then 98% purity has been achieved at 98% of peak recovery, provided the peaks are Gaussian and approximately equal in size. Baseline resolution requires that Rs >/= 1.5. At this value purity of the peak is 100%.

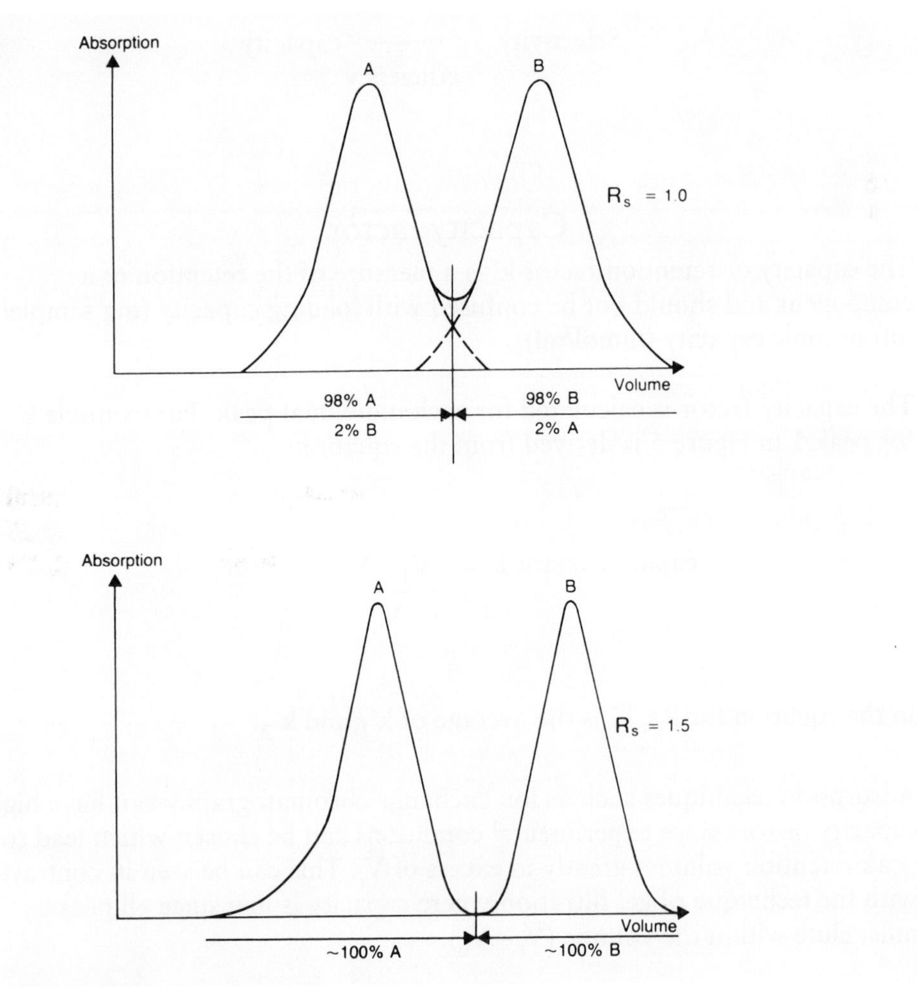

Fig. 4. Separation results with different resolutions.

Note: A completely resolved peak is not equivalent to a pure substance. This peak frequently represents a series of components which are not resolvable using the selected separation parameter.

The resolution achievable in a system is proportional to the product of the selectivity, the efficiency and the capacity of the system, the three most important parameters to control in column chromatography. The analytical expression for Rs is:

$$Rs = 1/4 \underbrace{\frac{(\alpha - 1)}{\alpha}}_{\text{Selectivity}} \underbrace{(\sqrt{N})}_{\text{efficiency}} \underbrace{\frac{k'}{(1 + k')}}_{\text{capacity}}$$

Capacity factor

The capacity or retention factor k´ is a measure of the retention of a component and should not be confused with loading capacity (mg sample/ml) or ionic capacity (mmol/ml).

The capacity factor is calculated for each individual peak. For example k´ for peak 1 in Figure 5 is derived from the equation:

$$\text{capacity factor } k' = \frac{V_1 - V_0}{V_0}$$

In the equation for Rs, k´ is the average of k'_1 and k'_2.

Adsorption techniques such as ion exchange chromatography can have high capacity factors since experimental conditions can be chosen which lead to peak retention volumes greatly in excess of V_t. This can be seen in contrast with the technique of gel filtration where capacity is low since all peaks must elute within the volume $(V_t - V_o)$.

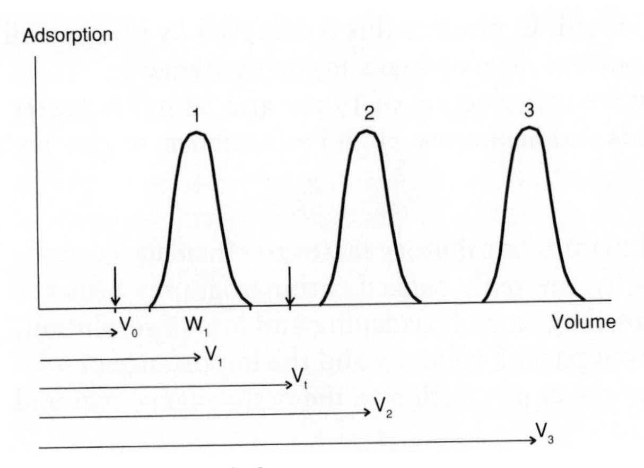

Fig. 5. Hypothetical chromatogram.
V_0 = void volume, V_1 = elution volume for peak 1, V_2 = elution volume for peak 2, V_t = total volume, W_1 = peak width for peak 1, W_2 = peak width for peak 2.

Efficiency

The efficiency factor N is a measure of the zone broadening which occurs on the column (peak width) and can be calculated from the expression:

$$N = 5.54 \left(\frac{V_1}{W_{1/2}}\right)^2$$

where $W_{1/2}$ is the peak width at half peak height

and is expressed as the number (N) of theoretical plates for the column under specified experimental conditions. Efficiency is frequently stated in the number of theoretical plates per metre chromatographic bed, or expressed as HETP (height equivalent to a theoretical plate), which is the bed length (L) divided by the plate number.

$$HETP = L/N$$

Since the observed value for N is dependent on experimental factors such as flow rate and sample loading, it is important that comparisons are done under identical conditions. In the case of ion exchange chromatography, efficiency is measured under isocratic conditions, using a substance which does not interact with the matrix e.g. acetone.

One of the main causes of zone broadening in a chromatography bed is longitudinal diffusion of the solute molecules. The diffusion effect is minimized if the distances available for diffusion, in both the liquid phase and the gel beads, are minimized. In practice this is achieved by using small uniform bead sizes and important developments in ion exchange chromatography have been the introduction of 10 µm and 34 µm diameter particles such as MonoBeads and Sepharose High Performance, to give high efficiency media.

After bead size, the second major contributory factor to efficiency is good experimental technique. Badly, unevenly packed chromatography beds and air bubbles will lead to chanelling, zone broadening and loss of resolution. Good separations require well packed columns and the importance of column packing increases in direct proportion to the performance required.

Selectivity

The selectivity (α) defines the ability of the system to separate peaks i.e. the distance between two peaks. The selectivity factor can be calculated from the chromatogram (Fig. 5) using the expression

$$\alpha = \frac{k'_2}{k'_1} = \frac{V_2 - V_0}{V_1 - V_0} = \text{approx.} \ \frac{V_2}{V_1}$$

Good selectivity is a more important factor than high efficiency in determining resolution (Fig. 6) since Rs is linearly related to selectivity but quadratically related to efficiency. This means that a four fold increase in efficiency is required to double the resolution under isocratic conditions.

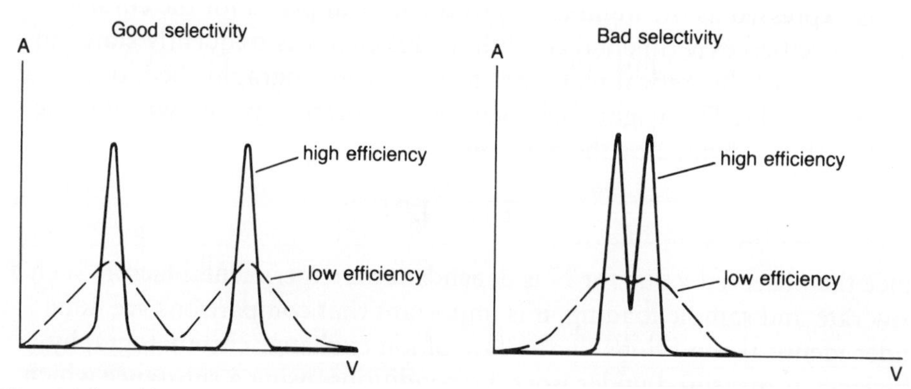

Fig. 6. The effect of selectivity and efficiency on resolution.

Selectivity in ion exchange chromatography is not only dependent on the nature and number of the ionic groups on the matrix but also on the experimental conditions, such as pH and ionic strength. It is the ease and predictability with which these experimental conditions, and thus the selectivity, can be manipulated which gives ion exchange chromatography the potential of extremely high resolution.

Capacity

The capacity of an ion exchanger is a quantitative measure of its ability to take up exchangeable counter-ions and is therefore of major importance. The capacity may be expressed as total ionic capacity, available capacity or dynamic capacity.

The total ionic capacity is the number of charged substituent groups per gram dry ion exchanger or per ml swollen gel. Total capacity can be measured by titration with a strong acid or base.

The actual amount of protein which can be bound to an ion exchanger, under defined experimental conditions, is referred to as the available capacity for the gel. If the defined conditions include the flow rate at which the gel is to be operated in a subsequent separation, the amount bound is referred to as the dynamic capacity for the ion exchanger. Available and dynamic capacities depend upon:

The properties of the protein.
The properties of the ion exchanger.
The chosen experimental conditions.

The properties of the protein which determine the available or dynamic capacity on a particular ion exchange matrix are its molecular size and its charge/pH relationship. The capacity of an ion exchanger is thus different for different proteins.

Since nearly all of the matrices used for ion exchange chromatography of biological molecules are porous, molecules which are small enough to enter the pores will exhibit a higher available capacity than those molecules which are restricted to the charged substituents on the surface of the gel.

Similarly, since the interaction is ionic the protein´s charge/pH relationship must be such that the protein carries the correct net charge, at a sufficiently high surface charge density to be bound to a particular ion exchanger under the chosen buffer conditions.

The properties of the ion exchange matrix which determine its available capacity for a particular protein are the exclusion limit of the matrix, and the type and number of the charged substituents. High available capacity is obtained by having a matrix which is macroporous and highly substituted with ionic groups which maintain their charge over a wide range of experimental conditions.

The experimental conditions which affect the observed capacity are pH, the ionic strength of the buffer, the nature of the counter-ion, the flow rate and the temperature. The flow rate is of particular importance with respect to dynamic capacity, which decreases as the flow rate is increased. These conditions should always be taken into consideration when comparing available capacities for different ion exchangers.

Methodologies for determining the available and dynamic capacities for an ion exchanger are given in Chapter 9.

3. Product Guide

Sephadex ion exchangers (pp. 19)

Sephadex ion exchangers are bead-formed media based on cross-linked dextran. They are available as strong and weak ion exchangers covering the range pH 2-10. Sephadex ion exchangers have excellent capacities for molecules with molecular weights up to 2×10^5. Supplied as dry powders in packs of 100 g and 500 g, Sephadex ion exchangers are suitable for batch-type separations.

DEAE Sephacel (pp. 24)

DEAE-Sephacel is a beaded cellulose ion exchanger for separations over a wide molecular weight range (up to 1×10^6 for globular proteins). DEAE Sephacel has good capacity over the range pH 2–9 and is supplied ready to use as a suspension in 24% ethanol, in packs of 500 ml.

DEAE Sepharose CL-6B, CM Sepharose CL-6B (pp. 31)

Sepharose ion exchangers are based on a cross-linked 6% agarose matrix. Traditionally, they have been used for ion exchange of proteins, polysaccharides, nucleic acids, membrane components and other high molecular weight substances. They have good flow properties and are supplied ready to use as a suspension in 20% ethanol, in packs of 500 ml.

Sepharose Fast Flow ion exchangers (pp. 34)

Sepharose Fast Flow ion exchangers are based on a highly cross-linked agarose matrix of high chemical and physical stability. The range consists of the weak exchangers DEAE Sepharose Fast Flow and CM Sepharose Fast Flow as well as the strong exchangers Q Sepharose and S Sepharose Fast Flow. Based on a 90 µm bead, Fast Flow ion exchangers give high resolution at high flow rates and are used at all scales from laboratory to process manufacturing scales.

Sepharose Fast Flow ion exchangers are supplied ready to use as a suspension in 20% ethanol, in packs of 500 ml. Q Sepharose and S

Sepharose Fast Flow are also available prepacked in HiLoad 16/10 and 26/10 columns.

Sepharose High Performance ion exchangers (pp. 37)

Strong exchanger groups Q and S coupled to a 34 μm highly crossed-linked agarose matrix, Q and S Sepharose High Performance represent state of the art ion exchange media for preparative separations. The 34 μm bead allows high efficiency separations without generating high back pressure. The gels are supplied prepacked in HiLoad 16/10 and 26/10 columns for ease of use, convenience and reproducibility. Ethanol, 20%, is used as a preservative.

MonoBeads (pp. 40)

Mono Q and Mono S are strong ion exchangers based on MonoBeads, a monodisperse 10 μm hydrophilic polymer matrix. Mono Q and Mono S are the established standards for high performance ion exchange separations. Supplied in prepacked high resolution columns containing 1.0 ml (HR 5/5), 8 ml (HR 10/10) and 20 ml (HR 16/10). Ethanol, 20%, is used as a preservative.

Bulk quantities

All Pharmacia LKB Biotechnology ion exchangers are available in larger pack sizes or larger prepacked columns. Please contact your local supplier of Pharmacia LKB Biotechnology products for further information.

Equipment

Pharmacia LKB Biotechnology supply a full range of equipment for operating all of the ion exchangers covered in this handbook.

Information regarding this equipment is to be found in the following literature, which is available upon request.

Standard Chromatography Instrument and System Guide.

FPLC for Protein Chromatography.

4. Sephadex ion exchangers

Sephadex ion exchangers are produced by introducing functional groups onto Sephadex, a cross-linked dextran matrix. These groups are attached to glucose units in the matrix by stable ether linkages.

Sephadex is suitable as a base for an ion exchanger matrix since it is hydrophilic and shows very low non-specific adsorption. Proteins, nucleic acids and other labile biological molecules are not adsorbed to or denatured by the gel. High degrees of substitution of Sephadex can be achieved without breakdown of the gel, so that high capacities are obtained.

Sephadex ion exchangers are derived from either Sephadex G-25 or G-50 and swell readily in aqueous solutions. Ion exchangers based on Sephadex G-25 are more tightly cross-linked than those based on Sephadex G-50 and therefore swell less and have greater rigidity. Ion exchangers based on Sephadex G-50 are more porous than those based on Sephadex G-25 and therefore have a better capacity for molecules with molecular weights larger than 30 000. The degree of swelling of Sephadex ion exchangers depends on the pH, the ionic strength of the buffers used, and the nature of the counter-ion and is not the same as that of the unsubstituted parent gel.

Sephadex is available with four different functional groups, giving a total of eight different ion exchangers. The full range of Sephadex ion exchangers is shown in Table 2.

Table 2. Sephadex ion exchangers.

Types		Description	Functional groups	Counter ion
DEAE Sephadex	A-25 A-50	Weakly basic anion exchanger	Diethylaminoethyl	Chloride
QAE Sephadex	A-25 A-50	Strongly basic anion exchanger	Diethy-(2-hydroxy-propyl)aminoethyl	Chloride
CM Sephadex	C-25 C-50	Weakly acidic cation exchanger	Carboxymethyl	Sodium
SP Sephadex	C-25 C-50	Strongly acidic cation exchanger	Sulphopropyl	Sodium

The letters A and C are added as suffixes to denote either anion or cation exchanger. They are used in conjunction with the numbers 25 and 50 to designate the parent Sephadex base.

Chemical stability

Sephadex ion exchangers are insoluble in all solvents. They are stable in water, salt solutions, organic solvents, alkaline and weakly acidic solutions. In strongly acidic solutions, hydrolysis of the glycosidic linkages may occur and thus pH values below 2 should be avoided, particularly at elevated temperatures. Sephadex ion exchangers can also be used in the presence of denaturing solvents which can be important when substances are to be separated on the basis of their electrostatic properties alone (6, 7, 8).

Exposure to strong oxidizing agents or dextranases should be avoided. During regeneration, the ion exchanger can be exposed for a short time to 0.01 M NaOH or 0.2 M HCI without appreciable hydrolysis. Prolonged exposure to high pH should be avoided due to the inherent instability of the DEAE group under these conditions. Sephadex ion exchangers are susceptible to attack by dextranases and should be stored in the presence of an antimicrobial agent (see page 89).

Physical stability

Swollen Sephadex ion exchangers can be sterilized by autoclaving for up to 30 min at 120°C, at neutral pH in the salt form. During autoclaving, minute quantities of carbohydrate are released; these can be washed away with sterile buffer.

Properties

Swelling

The swelling properties of Sephadex ion exchangers are related to those of the parent Sephadex G-types, those based on 50-types swelling more than those based on 25-types. Due to the presence of charged groups in the matrix, the swelling varies with ionic strength and pH.

Ionic strength dependence

At low ionic strengths, repulsion between groups carrying the same charge on the matrix is maximal, and swelling of the gel is at its greatest. The degree of swelling decreases with increasing ionic strength.

Note: Sephadex ion exchangers should not be swollen in distilled water since the bead structure may be broken down due to strong ionic interactions.

pH dependence

The degree of dissociation and hence the extent to which an ion exchanger is charged is dependent on pH. Repulsion between charged groups is greatest at pH values where the ion exchanger is fully dissociated, and decreases at pH values close to the pK of the charged groups.

Note: QAE Sephadex and SP Sephadex have swelling properties quite independent of pH since they are charged over a very wide pH range.

Capacity

Due to differences in swelling characteristics, ion exchangers based on Sephadex G-25 have a much higher ionic capacity per ml gel than those based on Sephadex G-50. (Table 3).

Table 3. Total capacity data for Sephadex ion exchangers.

Ion exchanger		Total capacity µmol/mg	Total capacity µmol/ml
DEAE	A-25	3.5+/- 0.5	500
Sephadex	A-50		175
QAE	A-25	3.0+/- 0.4	500
Sephadex	A-50		100
CM	C-25	4.5+/- 0.5	550
Sephadex	A-50		170
SP	A-25	2.3+/- 0.3	300
Sephadex	A-50		90

Thus for smaller proteins and polypeptides (MW < 30 000) the A-25 and C-25 types have a higher available capacity. In the molecular weight range 30 000 to 100 000 however, the A-50 and C-50 exchangers have higher available capacities due to their larger pore size.

If working with larger molecules (MW > 100 000), a higher available capacity is frequently observed with the A- and C-25 types since at these molecular weights binding is only occuring on the bead surface and the higher ionic capacity can be used to advantage.

As capacity also depends upon the number of substituent groups which are charged under given buffer conditions, it will also vary with pH. The variation of the charge on Sephadex ion exchangers with pH is illustrated by their titration curves (Fig. 7)

Available capacity data for Sephadex ion exchangers are given in Table 4.

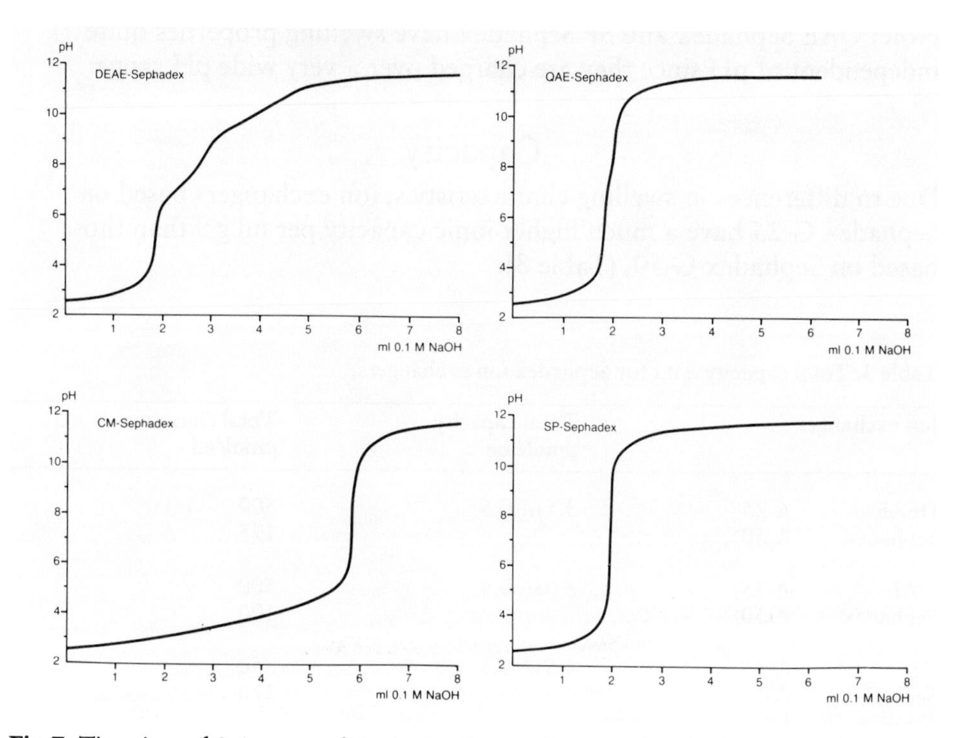

Fig.7. Titration of 0.1 gram of Sephadex ion exchangers in 50 ml 1 M KCl. (Work from Pharmacia, Uppsala, Sweden.).

Table 4. Available capacity (mg/ml) data for Sephadex ion exchangers.

Protein M.W.		Thyroglobulin 669000	HSA 68000	α-lactalbumin 143000	IgG 160000	Bovine COHb 69000
Ion exchanger						
DEAE	A-25	1.0	30.0	140.0	N.D.	N.D.
Sephadex	A-50	2.0	110.0	50.0	N.D.	N.D.
QAE	A-25	1.5	10.0	110.0	N.D.	N.D..
Sephadex	A-50	1.2	80.0	30.0	N.D.	N.D.
CM	C-25	N.D.	N.D.	N.D.	1.6	70.0
Sephadex	A-50	N.D.	N.D.	N.D.	7.0	140.0
SP	A-25	N.D.	N.D.	N.D.	1.1	70.0
Sephadex	A-50	N.D.	N.D.	N.D.	8.0	110.0

N.D. = Not determined
Capacities were determined using the method described in Chapter 9 at a flow rate of 75 cm/h. For anion exchangers (DEAE and QAE) the starting buffer was 0.05M Tris, pH 8.3 and for cation exchangers (CM and SP) 0.1 M acetate buffer, pH 5.0. Limit buffers were the respective start buffers containing 2.0 M NaCl.

Availability

Sephadex ion exchangers are supplied as dry powders in packs of 100 g and 500 g. Bulk quantities of 5 kg or more are available on request.

5. DEAE Sephacel

DEAE Sephacel is a bead-formed cellulose ion exchanger produced from high purity microcrystalline cellulose. Cellulose is a naturally occurring polymer consisting of β(1–4) linked glucose units. In the native state, adjacent polysaccharide chains are extensively hydrogen bonded, forming microcrystalline regions. These regions are interspersed with amorphous regions with less hydrogen bonding. Limited acid hydrolysis results in preferential loss of the amorphous regions and gives so-called microcrystalline cellulose.

During the production of DEAE Sephacel the microcrystalline structure is broken down and the cellulose is regenerated to give a bead-formed (40–160 μm) gel. The gel is strengthened by cross-linking with epichlorohydrin, although the main structure-forming bonds are still hydrogen bonds. Functional groups are attached during the synthesis by ether linkages to glucose units of the polysaccharide chains to give the structure shown in Figure 8.

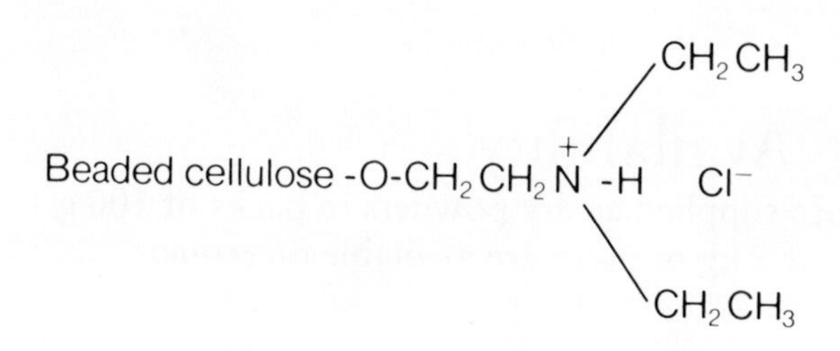

Fig. 8. Partial structure of DEAE-Sephacel.

After the introduction of cellulose based ion exchangers in 1956 (2), it was over a decade before cellulose ion exchangers were prepared in the optimal bead form (9). The physical form of cellulose ion exchangers is of great importance since the use of coarse fibrous forms leads to an increase in disturbances in flow and a reduction in the efficiency of the separation (10). A bead form is essential in order to obtain the best possible hydrodynamic and chromatographic properties. DEAE Sephacel is thus useful for consistent reliable laboratory separations of proteins, nucleic acids, hormones and other biopolymers when a cellulose based matrix is required.

Chemical stability

DEAE Sephacel is stable in aqueous suspension within the range pH 2–12. Hydrolysis may occur in strongly acidic solutions and the macromolecular structure is broken down in strongly alkaline solutions. The free base form of the DEAE group is inherently unstable at high pH values. Strong oxidizing agents should be avoided.

DEAE Sephacel is susceptible to microbial attack, especially in the presence of phosphates, and should therefore be stored in the presence of antimicrobial agents when not in use (page 89). Samples containing enzymes capable of hydrolysing β-glucosidic linkages should be purified on Sephadex, Sepharose or MonoBeads ion exchangers.

Physical stability

The cross-linked bead form of DEAE Sephacel gives it increased physical stability compared to ordinary microgranular celluloses. Thus DEAE Sephacel has excellent flow properties since the particles are less prone to break down and generate fines. It has a stable bed volume over a wide range of ionic strengths (approx. 5% change between $I = 0.05$ and $I = 0.5$) and pH values and can therefore be re-equilibrated in the column.

DEAE Sephacel can be sterilized by autoclaving at pH 7 for 30 minutes at 120° C. During autoclaving minute quantities of carbohydrate are released; these can be washed away with sterile buffer solution.

Properties

Swelling

DEAE Sephacel is supplied pre-swollen and is ready for use. As noted in the previous section, the bed volume changes very little with changes in pH or ionic strength.

Capacity

DEAE Sephacel is macroporous and has an exclusion limit of approximately 1×10^6 for proteins. The binding of substances with molecular weights substantially greater than 1×10^6 will be restricted to charged groups on the surface of the beads. Capacity data for DEAE Sephacel is summarized in Table 5.

Table 5. Capacity data for DEAE-Sephacel

	Ionic µmol/mg	Capacity µmol/ml	Available Capacity* mg/ml gel for albumin	thyroglobulin
DEAE Sephacel	1.4 ± 0.1	100–140	160	10

*Capacity was determined using the method described in Chapter 9 at a flow rate of 75 cm/h. The starting buffer was 0.05 M Tris, pH 8.3 Limit buffer was start buffers containing 2.0 M NaCl.

The adsorption kinetics for bead-formed cellulose ion exchangers are substantially the same as for conventional cellulose ion exchangers (9). As with other weak ion exchangers the capacity varies with pH. The titration curve for DEAE Sephacel is shown in Figure 9.

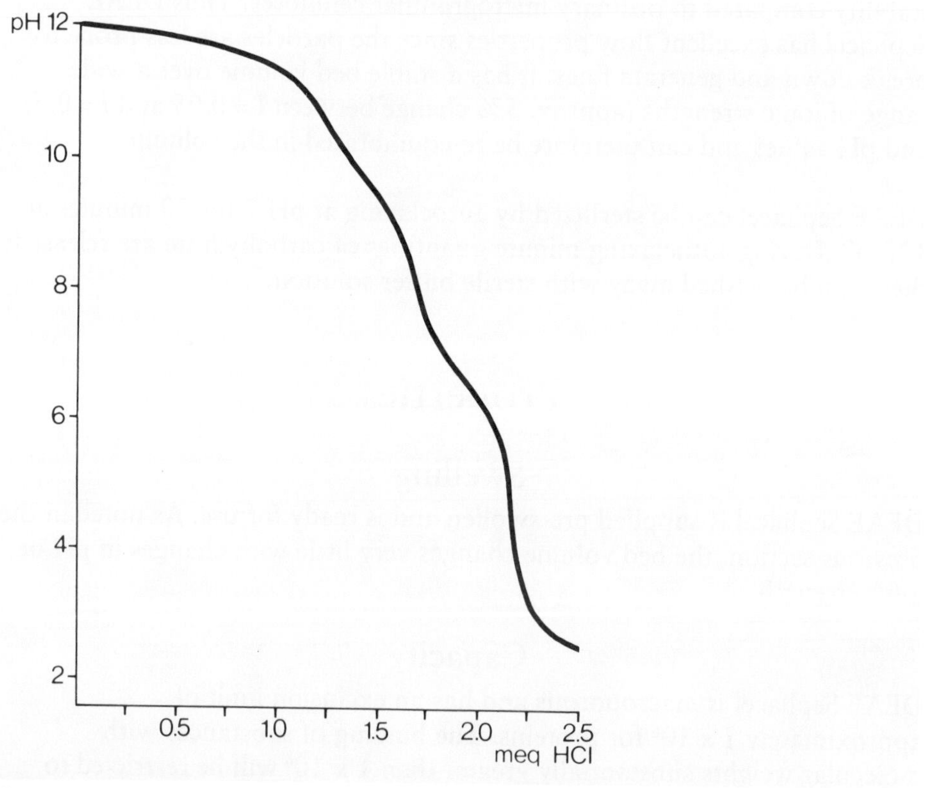

Fig. 9. Titration of 1 g DEAE Sephacel in 1 M KCl.(Work from Pharmacia, Uppsala, Sweden.).

Flow rates

The rigidity of DEAE Sephacel allows relatively high flow rates to be used. Figure 10 illustrates the variation of flow rate as a function of pressure drop for DEAE Sephacel.

As with other ion exchangers, resolution decreases with increasing flow rate. Flow rates of 10 cm/h are usually suitable for the resolution of protein mixtures on DEAE Sephacel. For applications requiring higher flow rates DEAE Sepharose Fast Flow should be used.

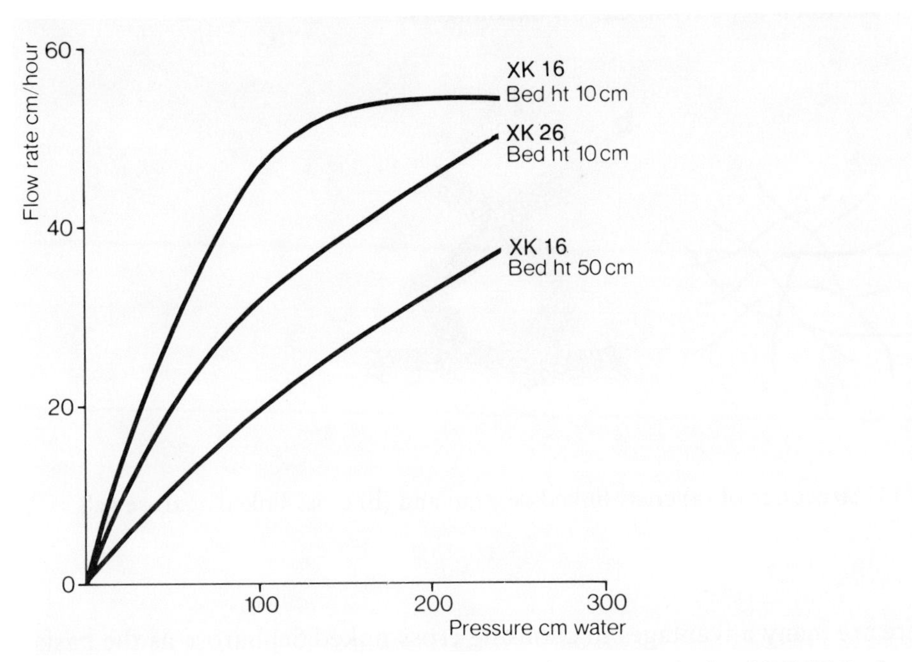

Fig.10. Flow rate as a function of the pressure drop across beds of DEAE Sephacel. 0.1 M Tris-HCl buffer solution pH 7.6. (Work from Pharmacia, Uppsala, Sweden.).

Availability

DEAE Sephacel is supplied in packs of 500 ml as a suspension in 24% ethanol.

6. Sepharose based ion exchangers

Pharmacia LKB Biotechnology offers a range of ion exchange media based on agarose, which is cross-linked to produce Sepharose CL-6B, Sepharose Fast Flow and Sepharose High Performance base matrices. Exchanger groups are then attached to the gel by stable ether linkages to the monosaccharide units to give the final ion exchange gels.

The modern Fast Flow and High Performance media give greatly improved performance in terms of flow rate and resolution respectively, compared to the traditional Sepharose CL-6B exchangers.

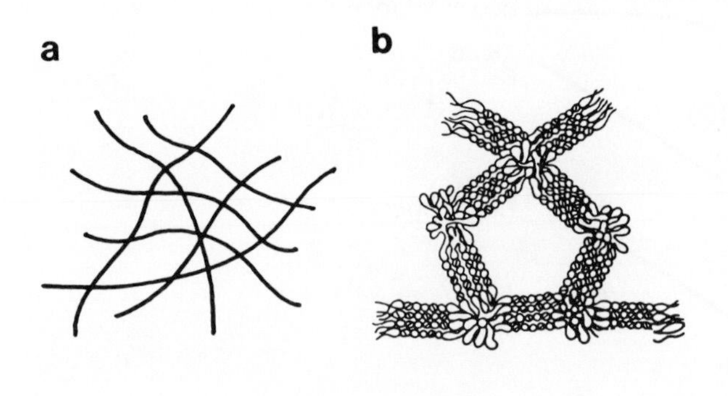

Fig. 11. Structures of (a) cross-linked dextran and (b) cross-linked agarose gels.

There are many advantages in choosing cross-linked Sepharose as the basis for ion exchange matrices. The Sepharose matrix has much greater rigidity for equivalent porosity than a Sephadex gel would have. This is due to the difference in macrostructure of the two gel types. In Sephadex the dextran chains are arranged in a random fashion, whilst in Sepharose the polysaccharide chains lie in bundles (Fig. 11). These bundles are further strengthened by different degrees of intra-chain cross-linking. The resulting structure is macroporous and the capacity of the gels very good for molecules up to 1×10^6 in molecular weight.

The gels, particularly in the Fast Flow and High Performance forms, have excellent flow properties and extremely stable bed volumes that are largely insensitive to changes in ionic strength and pH. They also show extremely low non-specific adsorption of macromolecules (11).

Chemical stability

Sepharose ion exchangers are insoluble in all solvents. They are stable in water, salt solutions, and organic solvents. All of the Sepharose based ion exchangers are stable in the range pH 2–14 for short periods e.g. washing. Details on the working pH range for each gel is given in the appropriate section below.

Prolonged exposure of DEAE Sepharose CL-6B or DEAE Sepharose Fast Flow to very alkaline conditions should be avoided because of the inherent instability of the DEAE group as a free base. The ion exchangers can be used in solutions of non-ionic detergents such as Triton X- 100® and with strongly dissociating solvents such as 8 M urea and 6 M guanidine hydrochloride (12). Under oxidizing conditions, limited hydrolysis of the polysaccharide chains may occur.

Sepharose is very resistant to microbial attack due to the presence of the unusual sugar, 3,6-anhydro-L-galactose. However, most buffers can support bacterial growth and so a bacteriostatic reagent should be used in storage (see page 89).

The gel-forming fibres of agarose are stiff bundles of polysaccharide chains rather than flexible single chains (13). For this reason the water in the gel can be replaced by other solvents with relatively little effect on pore size. Sepharose ion exchangers can be used in polar organic solvents and in aqueous/organic mixtures. The gel matrix is stable in a wide variety of solvents including ethanol, dimethylformamide, tetrahydrofuran, acetone, dimethylsulphoxide, chloroform, dichloromethane, dichloroethane and dichloroethane/pyridine (50:50).

Physical stability

The highly cross-linked structure of the modern Sepharose based ion exchangers not only gives them increased chemical stability but also results in improved physical stability. This improves flow properties enormously compared to normal Sepharose gels and prevents fluctuations in bed volume under conditions of increasing ionic strength. Thus Sepharose ion exchangers can be regenerated and re-equilibrated repeatedly in the column. Repacking between experiments is thus eliminated, improving reproducibility.

Sepharose ion exchangers can be used at temperatures up to 70°C and can be sterilized repeatedly in the salt form by autoclaving at pH 7 at temperatures of 110–120 °C.

DEAE Sepharose CL-6B and CM Sepharose CL-6B

DEAE Sepharose CL-6B and CM Sepharose CL-6B are macroporous bead-formed (45–165 μm diameter) ion exchangers derived from the cross-linked agarose gel Sepharose CL-6B (Fig. 12). DEAE or CM groups are then attached to the gel by ether linkages to the monosaccharide units to give the final ion exchange gel.

DEAE Sepharose CL-6B and CM Sepharose CL-6B have good chemical and physical stability and can be used to advantage in the ion exchange chromatography of proteins, polysaccharides, nucleic acids, membrane components and other high molecular weight substances.

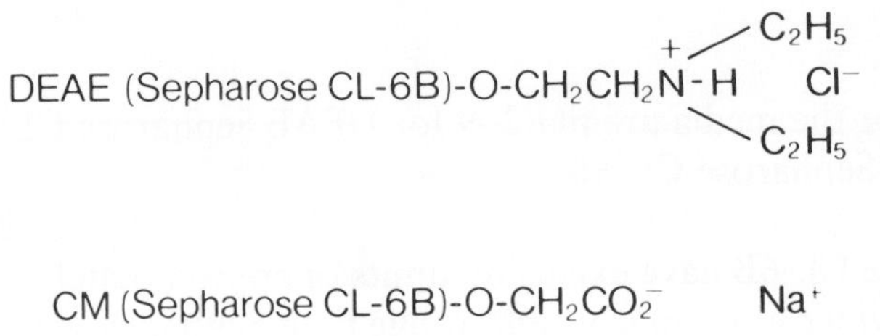

DEAE (Sepharose CL-6B)-O-$CH_2CH_2\overset{+}{N}H(C_2H_5)_2$ Cl^-

CM (Sepharose CL-6B)-O-$CH_2CO_2^-$ Na^+

Fig. 12. Partial structures of Sepharose CL-6B ion exchangers.

Properties

Swelling

DEAE and CM Sepharose CL-6B are supplied pre-swollen and ready for packing. As stated earlier, the cross-linked nature of the matrix means that the bed volume changes very little with changes in ionic strength or pH (approximately 2% change when the pH is reduced from 10 to 4).

Capacity

Since DEAE and CM Sepharose CL-6B are weak ion exchangers, the number of ligand groups which are charged and hence the capacity for macromolecules is dependent upon pH. This dependency is illustrated by the titration curves for DEAE and CM Sepharose CL-6B (Fig. 13).

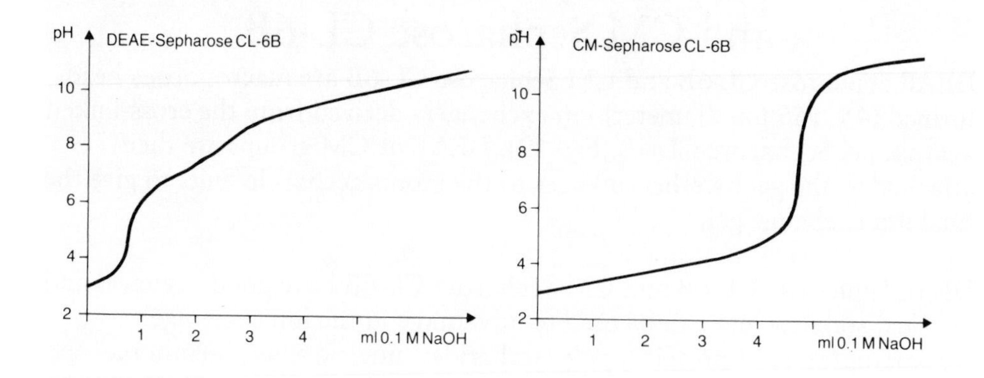

Fig. 13. Titration curves: approx. 5 ml. DEAE and CM Sepharose CL-6B both in 50 ml 1 M KCl. (Work from Pharmacia, Uppsala, Sweden.).

The working pH range for the media are pH 2–9 for DEAE Sepharose CL-6B and pH 6–10 for CM Sepharose CL-6B.

DEAE and CM Sepharose CL-6B have exclusion limits of approximately 4×10^6, so they cover a wider molecular weight range than Sephadex ion exchangers. The binding of substances with molecular weights substantially greater than $1 \times lO^6$ will be restricted to charged groups on the surface of the beads. Capacity data for Sepharose CL-6B ion exchangers are summarized in Table 6.

Table 6. Capacity data for Sepharose ion exchangers.*

	DEAE Sepharose CL-6B	CM Sepharose CL-6B
Ionic Capacity	130-170 µmol/ml	100-140 µmol/ml
Available Capacity (mg/ml)		
Thyroglobulin (669000)	2.0	N.D.
IgG (160000)	N.D.	9.5
Bovine COHb (69000)	N.D.	75
HSA (68000)	170	N.D.
α-lactalbumin (14300)	150	N.D.
Ribonuclease (13700)	N.D.	120

N.D = Not determined
*Capacities were determined using the method described in Chapter 9 at a flow rate of 75 cm/h. For the anion exchangers (DEAE) the starting buffer was 0.05M Tris, pH 8.3 and for the cation exchangers (CM) 0.1 M acetate buffer, pH 5.0. Limit buffers were the respective start buffers containing 2.0 M NaCl.

Flow rates

The cross-linked structure of Sepharose CL-6B ion exchangers allows flow rates of up to 100 cm/h to be used. During the chromatographic separation a maximum linear flow rate of not more than 60 cm/h is recommended. Figure 14 illustrates the variation of flow rate with pressure drop for DEAE and CM Sepharose CL-6B.

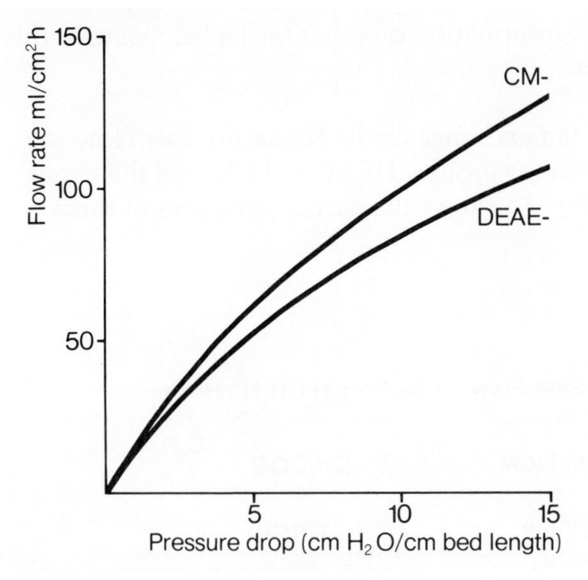

Fig. 14. Flow rate as a function of pressure drop in columns (5 x 10 cm bed volume) of DEAE and CM Sepharose CL-6B. pH 7.0; Ionic strength 0.02. (Work from Pharmacia, Uppsala, Sweden.).

As in all types of chromatography, resolution is dependent on flow rate (5). Therefore in applications where resolution is critically important high flow rates should be avoided or an exchanger based on Sepharose High Performance used.

For applications where high flow rates and large through-put of material are required, ion exchangers based on Sepharose Fast Flow should be used since these forms have been specially developed with these criteria in mind.

Availability

DEAE and CM-Sepharose CL-6B are supplied as suspensions in 20% ethanol in packs of 500 ml and 10 l.

Sepharose Fast Flow ion exchangers

Sepharose Fast Flow Ion Exchangers are also based on 45–165 μm agarose beads. However, a higher degree of cross-linking is used to give the media greatly improved physical and chemical stability. This high stability allows the gels to be used at the higher flow rates required for modern laboratory separations as well as meeting the through-put and cleaning-in-place requirements of process scale chromatography. These media are part of the the BioProcess Media family. Information on other media belonging to this group is available on request.

To give a complete range of ion exchange media Sepharose Fast Flow is available with the weak exchanger groups, DEAE and CM and the strong exchanger groups Q and S. Fig. 15 shows the partial structures of these media.

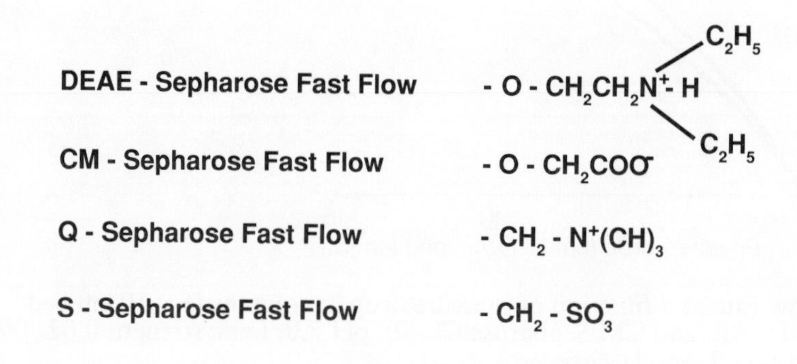

Fig. 15. Partial structure of Sepharose Fast Flow ion exchange media

Properties

Swelling

Sepharose Fast Flow ion exchangers are supplied pre-swollen and ready for packing or in prepacked columns. The average bead diameter is 90 μm with a bead size distribution of 45–165 μm. The highly cross-linked nature of the matrix means that the bead size and bed volumes do not change with changes in ionic strength or pH.

Capacity

As is the case with all ion exchangers the capacity is dependent upon the accessibility of the charged groups and their number. Sepharose Fast Flow ion exchangers are highly substituted and have an exclusion limit of approximately 4 x 10^6 giving high capacity for proteins. Capacity data for Fast Flow ion exchange media are given in Table 7.

Table 7. Capacity data for Sepharose Fast Flow matrices

Ion Exchanger	Q Sepharose Fast Flow	S Sepharose Fast Flow
Total capacity (μmol/ml)	180-250	180-250
Available capacity (mg/ml)*		
Thyroglobulin	3	N.D.
HSA	120	N.D.
α-lactalbumin	110	N.D.
IgG	N.D.	50
Bovine COHb	N.D.	50
Ribonuclease	N.D.	70

Ion Exchanger	DEAE Sepharose Fast Flow	CM Sepharose Fast Flow
Total capacity (μmol/ml)	110-160	90-130
Available capacity (mg/ml)*		
Thyroglobulin	3.1	N.D.
HSA	110	N.D.
α-lactalbumin	100	N.D.
IgG	N.D.	15
Bovine COHb	N.D.	30
Ribonuclease	N.D.	50

N.D = Not determined
*Capacities were determined using the method described in Chapter 9 at a flow rate of 75 cm/h. For anion exchangers (DEAE and Q) the starting buffer was 0.05M Tris, pH 8.3 and for cation exchangers (CM and S) 0.1 M acetate buffer, pH 5.0. Limit buffers were the respective start buffers containing 2.0 M NaCl.

Q Sepharose Fast Flow and S Sepharose Fast Flow are highly substituted with strong ion exchange groups. These groups remain charged and maintain consistently high capacities over broad working pH ranges of 3–11 and 4–11 respectively. This allows the selection of a pH value and buffer that best suit the properties of the sample. Titration curves for both gels are shown in Figure 16. The working pH ranges for DEAE Sepharose Fast Flow and CM Sepharose Fast Flow are pH 2–9 and pH 6–10 respectively.

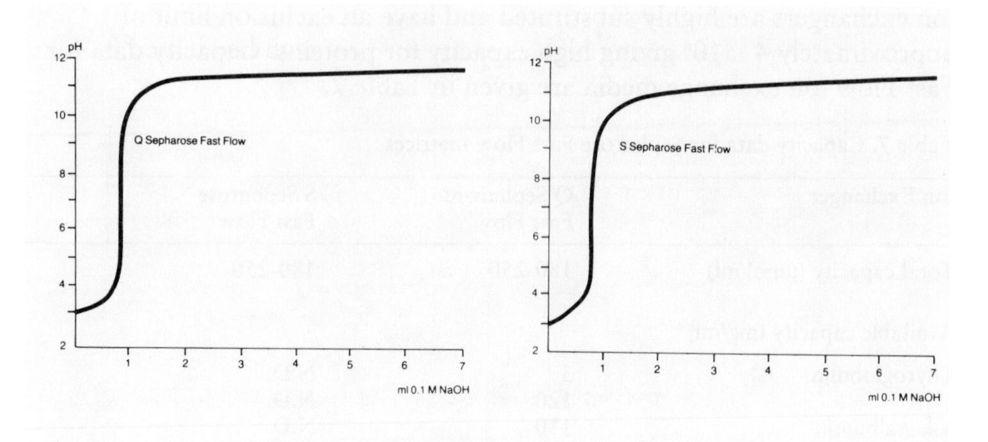

Fig. 16. Titration curves; approx. 5 ml Q and S Sepharose Fast Flow in 50 ml 1 M KCl. (Work from Pharmacia, Uppsala, Sweden.).

Flow rates

The optimal cross-linking of Sepharose Fast Flow confers excellent flow properties on the matrix. This is illustrated in Figure 17 which shows the relationship between flow rate and operating pressure for a number of commercially available ion exchange matrices.

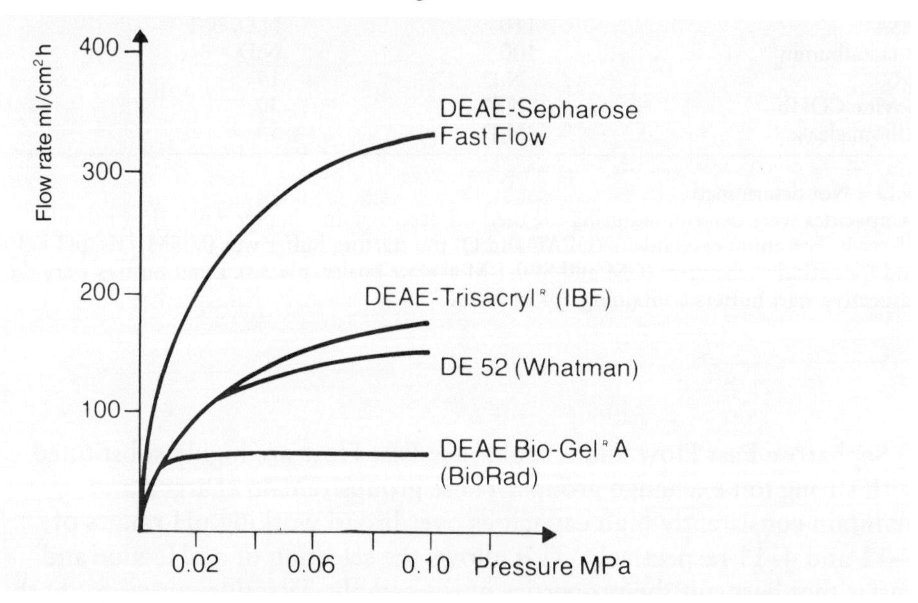

Fig. 17. Flow rate comparisons of DEAE Sepharose Fast Flow with other commercially available DEAE substituted ion exchangers. Column: Pharmacia XK 50/30 fitted with 1/4 inch tubing. Gel bed height 15 cm. Gel bed volume 29.4 ml. Eluent 0.1 M NaCl. (Work from Pharmacia, Uppsala, Sweden.).

Flow rates achievable with Fast Flow media are up to 400 cm/h at 0.1 MPa (1 bar) in a XK 50/30 column packed with a 15 cm high bed of gel. In laboratory separations where the best possible separation is frequently a major consideration this flow rate is frequently traded off against improved resolution. In industrial processing, the high throughput properties of Sepharose Fast Flow ion exchangers give significantly reduced cycle times and improved productivity.

Availability

DEAE and CM Sepharose Fast Flow are available in packs of 500 ml and 10 l.

Q and S Sepharose Fast Flow are available in packs of 300 ml and 5 l and prepacked in HiLoad 16/10 and 26/10 columns. In all cases 20 % ethanol is used as a preservative.

Sepharose High Performance ion exchangers

Sepharose High Performance ion exchange media are based on 34 μm highly cross-linked agarose beads. The small uniform bead-size gives the media high efficiency (12 000 theoretical plates per metre), which in combination with high selectivity offers the possibility of high resolution standard chromatography separations.

In addition, the use of identical functional groups to those used in Q and S Sepharose Fast Flow and Mono Q and Mono S media, at comparable substitution levels (i.e. same selectivity), simplifies scaling up from FPLC and up to BioPilot and BioProcess scales.

Q - Sepharose High Perfomance $-CH_2-N^+(CH)_3$

S - Sepharose High Performance $-CH_2-SO_3^-$

Fig. 18. Partial structure of Sepharose High Performance ion exchange media

Properties

Chemical stability

Q Sepharose High Performance and S Sepharose High Performance have high chemical stability due to the highly cross-linked agarose matrix. They can be used in aqueous salt solutions in the range pH 2–12 and pH 3–12 respectively for continuous operation, and over the pH range 2–14 for cleaning procedures. They are stable in strongly dissociating solvents such as 8 M urea and 6 M guanidine hydrochloride. The media also tolerate 1 M acetic acid, 30% isopropanol, 30% acetonitrile, 24% ethanol and 1 M NaOH. Under oxidizing conditions, limited hydrolysis of the polysaccharide chains may occur.

Physical stability

The high degree of cross-linking of Sepharose High Performance renders the media extremely stable physically. The high rigidity of the cross-linked agarose matrix eliminates volume variations due to changes in pH or ionic strength, and confers excellent flow properties. This rigidity together with the small particle size distribution of the 34 µm beads means that working flow rates up to 150 cm/h can be employed.

Capacity

As is the case with all ion exchangers, the capacity depends upon the accessibility of the charged groups and their number. Sepharose High Performance gels have an exclusion limit of approximately 4×10^6 and are highly substituted with strong ion exchange groups. Thus they remain charged and maintain consistently high capacities for proteins over a broad working pH range (Table 8). This allows the selection of a pH value and buffer that best suit the properties of the sample. Titration curves for Q and S Sepharose High Performance are similar to those for Q and S Sepharose Fast Flow, which are shown in Figure 16.

Total ionic capacity can be measured by titration with a strong acid or base. Details of the ionic capacities for the media are shown in Table 8.

The available capacity varies from case to case depending on protein properties and flow rate, but a typical dynamic capacity for bovine serum albumin on Q Sepharose High Performance is greater than 90 mg per ml gel at 150 cm/h (start buffer 0.15 M Tris, pH 7.15, limit buffer = start buffer plus 0.8 M NaCl).

The characteristics of the prepacked columns and media are shown in Table 8.

Table 8. Characteristics of HiLoad Q and S Sepharose High performance

Product	Q Sepharose HP		S Sepharose HP	
HiLoad	16/10	26/10	16/10	26/10
Type	strong anion	strong anion	strong cation	strong cation
Ionic capacity (mmol/ml)	0.14-0.20	0.14-0.20	0.14-0.20	0.14-0.20
Bed volume ml	20-22	53-58	20-22	53-58
Flow rate (25°C) cm/h*	up to 150	up to 150	up to 150	up to 150
Max pressure	3 bar	3 bar	3 bar	3 bar
Theoretical Plates per m (N/m)**	>12000	>12000	>12000	>12000
Approx. mean particle size	34 um	34 um	34 um	34 um
Particle size range um	24-44	24-44	24-44	24-44
pH working range	2-12	2-12	3-12	3-12
pH cleaning range***	2-14	2-14	2-14	2-14

* Max. pressures and flow rates should not be used routinely.
** Determined with acetone.
*** 1 M NaOH and 1 M acetic acid should only be used in cleaning procedures.

Availability

To ensure optimal performance and reproducibility Sepharose High Performance media are supplied in prepacked HiLoad Columns with dimensions 16 and 26 mm in internal diameter and 10 cm in length. The media is also available in prepacked columns of 100 ml (35/100) and 300 ml (60/100) for BioPilot scale separations.

7. MonoBeads

MonoBeads are unique, highly efficient, pH stable ion exchange media, specifically designed for fast high resolution separations of proteins, peptides, and oligonucleotides. An example of the type of separation which can be achieved is shown in Figure 19.

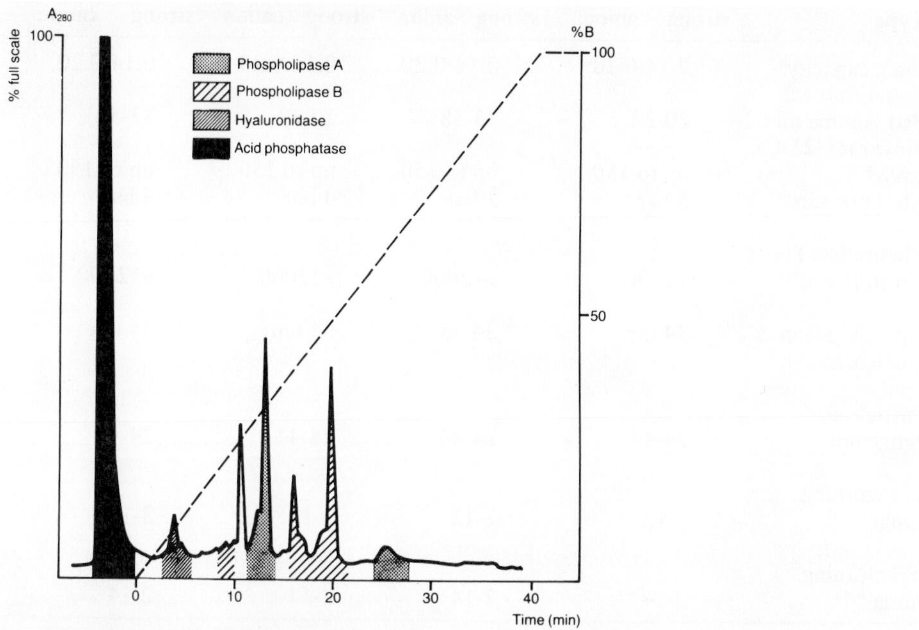

Fig. 19. Characterization of venom from the White Faced Hornet by cation exchange chromatography (14).
Conditions: Venom (7 mg) dissolved in 50 mM BICINE, pH 8.4 (buffer A); Column, Mono S HR 5/5; Buffer B, 0.35 M NaCl in Buffer A; Gradient, 0-100% B in 40 ml; flow rate, 1 ml/min; detection, 280 nm at 0.05 AUFS.

MonoBeads ion exchangers are based on a 10 µm beaded hydrophylic polyether resin which has been substituted with quaternary amine groups to yield the strong anion exchanger, Mono Q, or with methyl sulphonate groups to yield the strong cation exchanger, Mono S.

Note: Substitution with the same ionic groups as Polybuffer Exchanger PBE 94 gives Mono P – the matrix used for high resolution chromatofocusing. For further information on the technique and media for chromatofocusing the reader should contact Pharmacia LKB Biotechnology.

The name MonoBeads is derived from the unique monodisperse nature of the matrix. MonoBeads have the narrowest particle size distribution available for chromatographic matrices (10 +/– 0.03 µm). This monodispersity (Fig. 20) was accomplished through a process developed by Professor John Ugelstad of SINTEF, Trondheim, Norway.

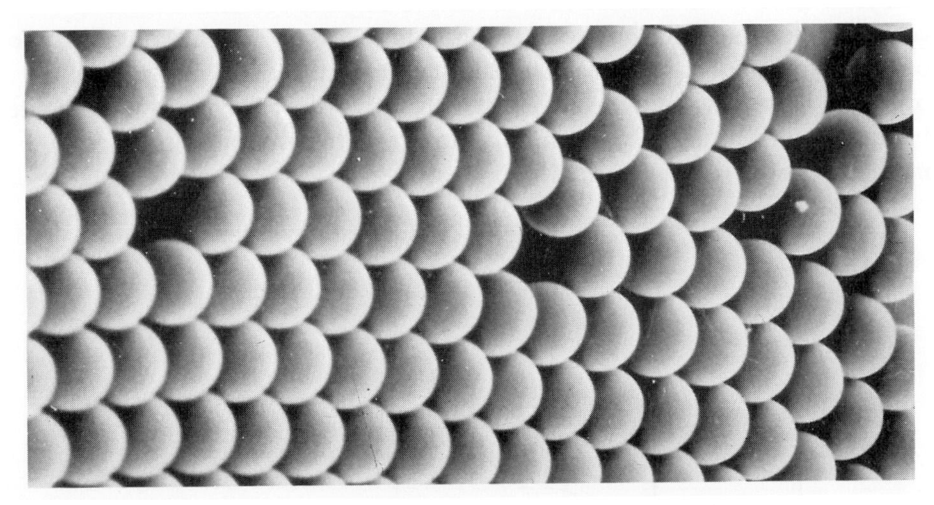

Fig. 20. An electron micrograph of MonoBeads showing their distinct monodispersity.

The resolution which can be achieved on any chromatographic matrix is a result of a combination of the efficiency and selectivity of the system. Maximum efficiency is obtained through the use of small, perfectly spherical, monodisperse particles, optimally packed in a well designed column. The 10 µm monodisperse MonoBeads matrix gives efficiencies as high as 46 000 plates per metre under isocratic elution (15). High efficiency, coupled with the excellent selectivity of the Q and S substituents results in the high resolution separations characteristic of FPLC technology.

Scale-up to Q and S Sepharose High Performance and Q and S Sepharose Fast Flow is simple since these gels have similar selectivities to the MonoBeads based media.

Properties

Chemical stability

The gels are stable for continuous use in the pH range 2 to 12, although pH values as high as 14 can be used during cleaning and sanitizing procedures. MonoBeads can be used with solutions of most buffers used in biochemical separations of proteins and peptides and in water-alcohol (C1 – C4) and acetonitrile-water solutions.

The resistance of the MonoBeads matrix to organic solvents allows complete cleaning and the use of conditions necessary for the solubilization of very hydrophobic samples. An example of the use of MonoBeads with organic solvents is given in Fig. 21, which shows the analysis of the peptide bacitracin on Mono S using lithium chlorate as the eluting salt and 90% methanol as the liquid phase (15).

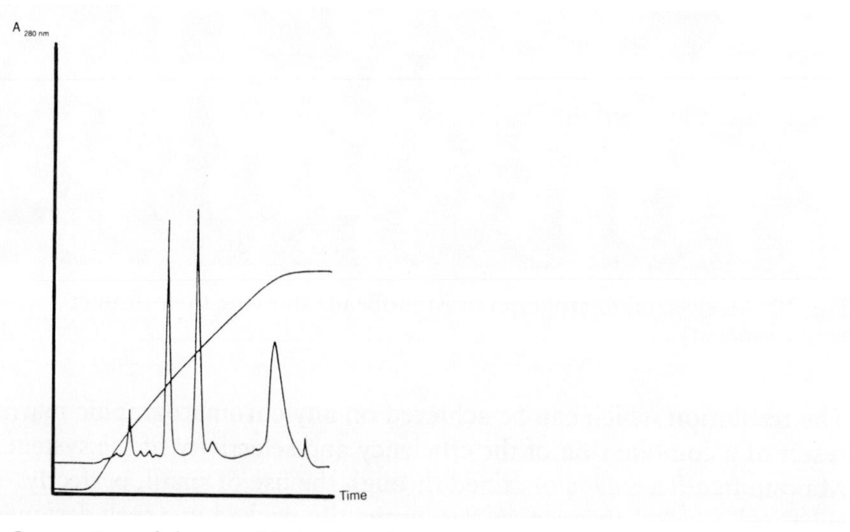

Fig. 21. Separation of the peptide bacitracin on Mono S. (Work from Pharmacia, Uppsala, Sweden.).

Dimethylsulphoxide (DMSO) and similar solvents will change the separation properties of the gels. Aqueous solutions of urea, ethylene glycol and similar compounds can be used but will increase the back pressures due to their higher viscosities. Non-ionic detergents, zwitterionic detergents or detergents with the same charge as the ion exchange groups may be used. Oxidising agents should be avoided.

Physical stability

MonoBeads are based on highly rigid beads which means that they can be used at high flow rates. As a consequence of the monodisperse nature of the matrix these high flow rates do not result in high back pressures. For example an HR 5/5 column (5 mm x 5 cm) packed with a MonoBeads matrix normally generates a back pressure of 1.0–1.5 MPa (10–15 bar) when operated at a flow rate of 1 ml/min (300 cm/h).

Note: These back pressures are beyond the operating limits of standard laboratory peristaltic pumps.

A summary of the chemical and physical properties of MonoBeads is shown in Table 9.

Table 9. Chemical and physical properties of MonoBeads

Properties	**Mono Q**	**Mono S**
Type of gel	strong anion exchanger	strong cation exchanger
Charged group	$-CH_2N^+(CH_3)_3$	$-CH_2SO_3^-$
Ionic capcity mmoles/ml of gel	0.32±0.05 (Cl^-)	0.16±0.02 (Na^+)
Column dimensions		
HR 5/5	5 x 50 mm	5 x 50 mm
HR 10/10	10 x 100 mm	10 x 100 mm
HR 16/10	16 x 100 mm	16 x 100 mm
Average particle size (μm)	10±0.5	10±0.5
Standard deviation (μm)	≤0.3	≤0.3
MW range (proteins)	up to 10^7	up to 10^7
pH stability (cleaning)	2–12	2–12
pH stability (working range)	3–11	3–11
Pressure limit of column		
HR 5/5	10 MPa	10 MPa
HR 10/10	5 MPa	5 MPa
HR 16/10	3 MPa	3 MPa
Max recommended operating pressure		
HR 5/5	5 MPa	5 MPa
HR 10/10	4 MPa	4 MPa
HR 16/10	3 MPa	3 MPa

Solvent restrictions
The columns are stable in alcohol/water solutions (C_1–C_4). 100 % Dimethyl sulphoxide, dimethylformamide, and formic acid can change the separation properties of the gel. Avoid oxidixing and reactive reagents. Detergents can be used if they are non-ionic or have the same charge as the gel.

Flow rate

The rigid monodisperse nature of the media enables high flow rates to be used on MonoBeads columns. Normal recommended flow rates for high resolution separations are in the range 150 to 600 cm/h for HR5/5 columns. Higher flow rates can be used during column washing and regeneration.

In addition, the absence of buffering capacity means that buffer exchange and re-equilibration can be executed quickly and with small amounts of buffer. Details of the recommended flow rates to be used on the different columns are given in Table 10.

Capacity

MonoBeads ion exchangers are highly substituted with ionic groups giving high ionic capacities. For Mono Q the ionic capacity is 0.32 +/– 0.05 mmoles per ml gel (Cl^-) and for Mono S 0.16 +/– 0.02 mmoles per ml gel (Na^+).

The high substitution levels coupled with the large pore size of the matrix, the exclusion limit for globular proteins is 10^7, give MonoBeads exchangers high capacities for large proteins as well as for smaller polypeptides and peptides.

Table 10. Chromatographic properties of pre-packed columns of MonoBeads.

Properties	Mono Q HR 5/5	Mono Q HR 10/10	Mono Q HR 16/10	Mono S HR 5/5	Mono S HR 10/10	Mono S HR 16/10
Max. loading capacity						
mg/column	25	200	500	25	200	500
mg/peak	5	40	100	5	40	100
Typical total protein binding capacity (mg/column)						
Human serum albumin (HSA)	65	500	1 300			
Immunoglobulin G (IgG)				75	600	1 500
Typical protein recoveries (%)		90–100			90–100	
Typical enzyme activity recoveries (%)		>80			>80	
Recommended flow rates (ml/min)	0.5–2.0	4	10	0.5–2	4	10
Normal separation times (min)	5–20	40	40	5–20	40	40

Typical saturation capacities are in the range of 60 mg protein per ml of gel and typical sample loading capacities are in the region of 25 mg of protein per ml of gel. Data on the saturation and loading capacities for some specific proteins are given in Table 10.

The titration curves for Mono Q and Mono S (Fig. 22.) show no buffering capacity which means that the loading capacity does not vary with pH over the working range of the gel.

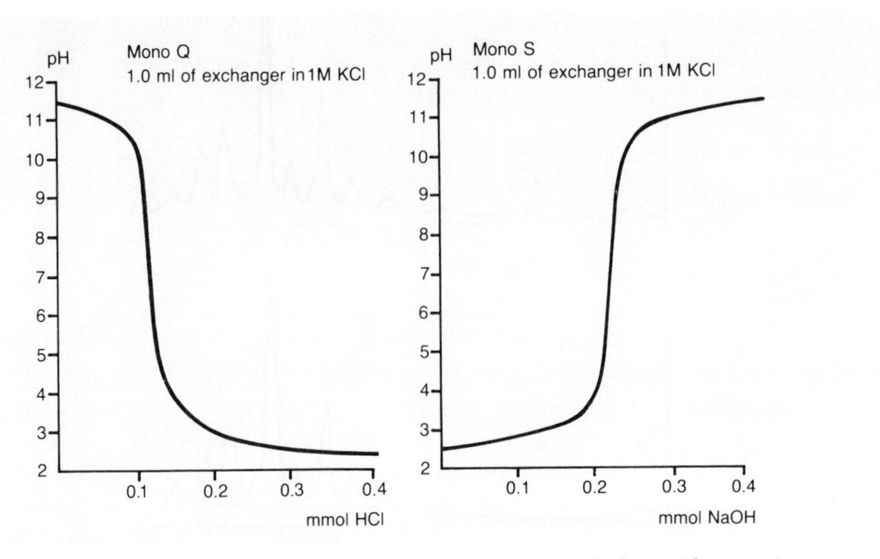

Fig. 22. Titration curves for Mono Q and Mono S. (Work from Pharmacia, Uppsala, Sweden.).

Recovery

Non-specific interactions to the MonoBeads matrix are very low and consequently recoveries are high. Recoveries of protein mass are typically 90–100% and of protein activity greater than 80%. Examples of protein activity recoveries are shown in Table 11.

Table 11. Protein activity recoveries(%) from MonoBeads columns

Protein	Mono Q	Mono S
β-Glucuronidase	106	N.D.
β-Glucosidase	N.D.	93
Phosphodiesterase	80	N.D.
Creatine Kinase	90	N.D.
Enolase	N.D.	95
Lactate Dehydrogenase	N.D.	102
Aldolase	N.D.	94

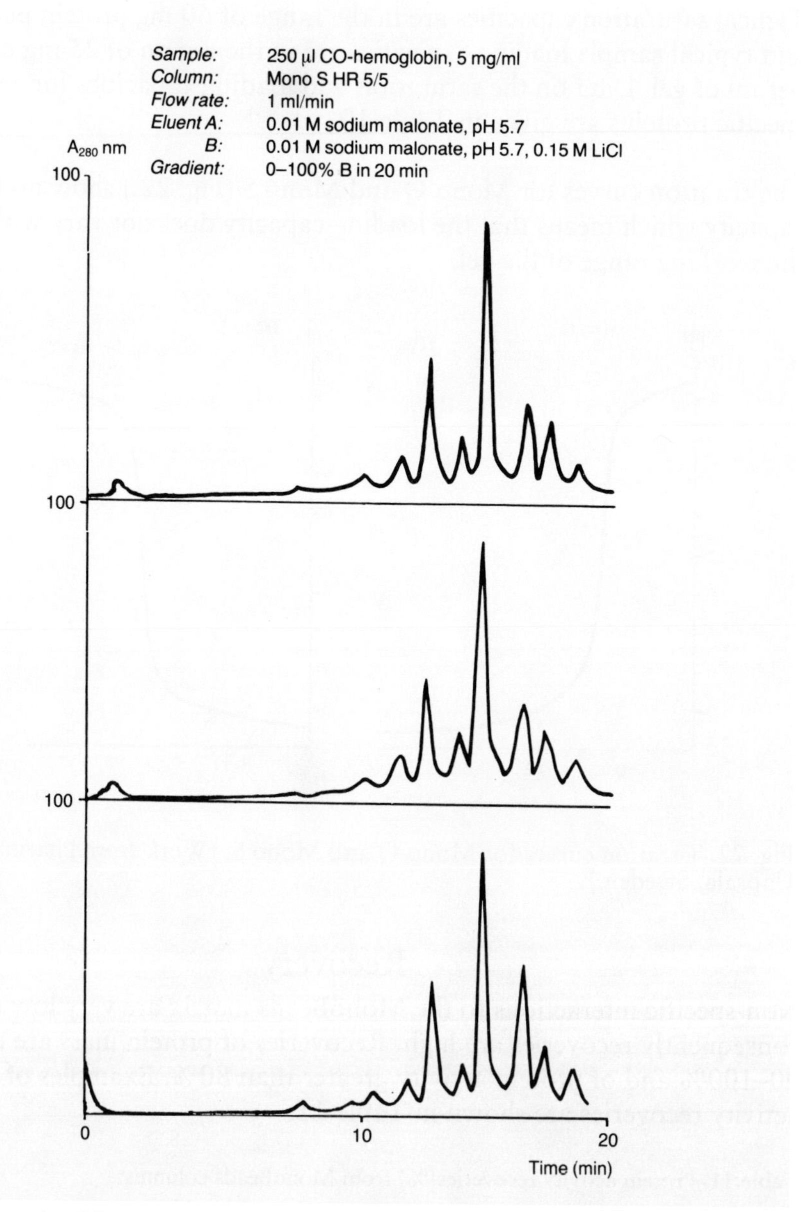

Fig. 23. Reproducible separations on three Mono S HR 5/5 columns. (Work from Pharmacia, Uppsala, Sweden.).

Reproducibility

The stability of the MonoBeads matrix together with controlled synthesis and column packing procedures ensure very reproducible separations both over time and from column to column. Figure 23 shows the reproducibility of a separation performed on three different Mono S columns.

Availability

Mono Q and Mono S are available prepacked in columns HR 5/5, HR 10/10 and HR 16/10 containing 1, 8 and 20 ml of gel respectively. Mono Q and Mono S 35/100 and 60/100 columns, containing 100 and 300 ml of gel are also available for chromatography at BioPilot scale.

8. Experimental Technique I

Choice of ion exchanger

No single ion exchanger is best for every separation. The choice of matrix and ionic substituent depends on:

1. The specific requirements of the application.
2. The molecular size of the sample components.
3. The isoelectric points of the sample components

Specific requirements of the application.

Column or batch separation.

If the separation is to be carried out using a batch separation technique rather than column chromatography, the flow and packing characteristics of the matrix are of minor importance. The economy and high capacity of Sephadex based ion exchangers make them a natural choice.

The scale of the separation

The amount of sample to be processed is an important parameter when choosing an ion exchange medium. For laboratory scale separations any of the Pharmacia LKB range of ion exchangers can be used. However for large scale separations, which must satisfy the through-put and cleaning in place (CIP) requirements of industry, the choice of a Sepharose Fast Flow based exchanger is indicated.

The same reasoning applies to experiments designed as method scouting separations for eventual scale-up since such procedures should be developed using the gel which will eventually be used at the larger scale. Sepharose Fast Flow based exchangers are extremely well suited to this type of method optimization as well as routine laboratory separations.

The required resolution

When choosing an ion exchanger it is important to decide the degree of resolution required from the separation. Normally analytical or semi-analytical separations place high demands on resolution. In contrast, resolution is frequently traded off against capacity and speed in the case of preparative work.

Resolution in ion exchange chromatography depends upon the selectivity and efficiency of the media. Maximum selectivity is usually obtained by choosing one of the gels carrying the strong exchanger groups Q or S, since strong ion exchangers can be used at any pH tolerated by the sample molecules.

Maximum efficiency is obtained by choosing a gel based on a small particle size matrix. The media in order of their particle sizes and potential efficiencies are MonoBeads (10 µm) > Sepharose High Performance (34 µm) > Sepharose Fast Flow/ Sepharose CL-6B/ Sephacel (90 µm) > Sephadex (40-125 µm in dry form).

The media thus offering the highest degree of resolution are the MonoBeads exchangers for high resolution FPLC and Sepharose High Performance exchangers for high resolution standard chromatography.

The required through-put.

How much material which can be processed in a defined time is determined amongst other things by the capacity, the flow characteristics of the media and the size of the column. All of the ion exchangers available from Pharmacia LKB Biotechnology have high capacities for macromolecules but differ considerably in their flow properties. The media which have optimal flow characteristics are MonoBeads for high performance, FPLC separations, and Sepharose High Performance and Fast Flow media for laboratory and process scale preparative separations.

Scaleabilty

Frequently ion exchange separations are carried out initially on a small scale to optimize conditions before commiting the sample to full scale separations. It is thus important to choose an ion exchanger which will allow simple and convenient scale up so that methods established on a small column can be applied more or less directly to the larger column. Detailed information on scaling-up ion exchange separations is given in Chapter 9.

Reproducibility

Reproducibility is obtained when the characteristics of the chromatography bed remain unchanged during the course of the separation and during regeneration of the column. All Pharmacia LKB ion exchange media, with the exception of those based on Sephadex, can be washed and regenerated in the column. In addition, the more rigid varieties such as Sepharose High

Performance, Sepharose Fast Flow and MonoBeads show no changes in bed size with changes in pH and ionic strength, giving additional reproducibility.

The use of media which are supplied prepacked and tested, such as MonoBeads and Sepharose High Performance assures reproducibility since variability in column packing is eliminated

Economy

Column or batch procedures in which the ion exchanger is used once and thrown away, as well as applications requiring large amounts of gel, may make economy a major consideration. Sephadex A-50 and C-50 ion exchangers are the least expensive in terms of bed volume, followed by Sephadex A-25 and C-25 ion exchangers.

The molecular size of the sample components

The accessibility of the sample components to the charged groups will determine the available capacity of the ion exchanger for those particular substances. All of the ion exchange media supplied by Pharmacia, with the exception of Sephadex based media, have exclusion limits for globular proteins in excess of 1×10^6.

Steric factors only affect the separation of charged solutes via their influence on the available capacity for each substance. When choosing ion exchangers it is unnecessary to consider the possibility of gel filtration effects on the sample. Sample molecules, although always larger than those of the eluent buffer, cannot migrate ahead of the eluting buffer since they then encounter conditions which favour their re-binding to the matrix. Only uncharged solutes will be fractionated according to size as in gel filtration. These uncharged molecules will normally be removed during the initial isocratic elution phase which proceeds the application of the gradient.

The exclusion limits for the different media and subsequent effects on available capacity are given in the relevant sections covering each gel type.

When working with samples of unknown molecular weight the use of Sepharose and MonoBeads based ion exchangers is recommended since they are particularly easy to handle and have good capacities over a large MW range. Sepharose Fast Flow ion exchangers can be used with very high flow rates for rapid separations and are also most suitable for scaling up to large scale usage.

Choice of exchanger group

Substances are bound to ion exchangers when they carry a net charge opposite to that of the ion exchanger. This binding is electrostatic and reversible.

In the case of substances which carry only one type of charged group the choice of ion exchanger is clear-cut. Substances which carry both positively and negatively charged groups, however, are termed amphoteric and the net charge which they carry depends on pH (Fig. 24). Consequently at a certain pH value an amphoteric substance will have zero net charge. This value is termed the isoelectric point (pI) and at this point substances will bind to neither anion or cation exchangers.

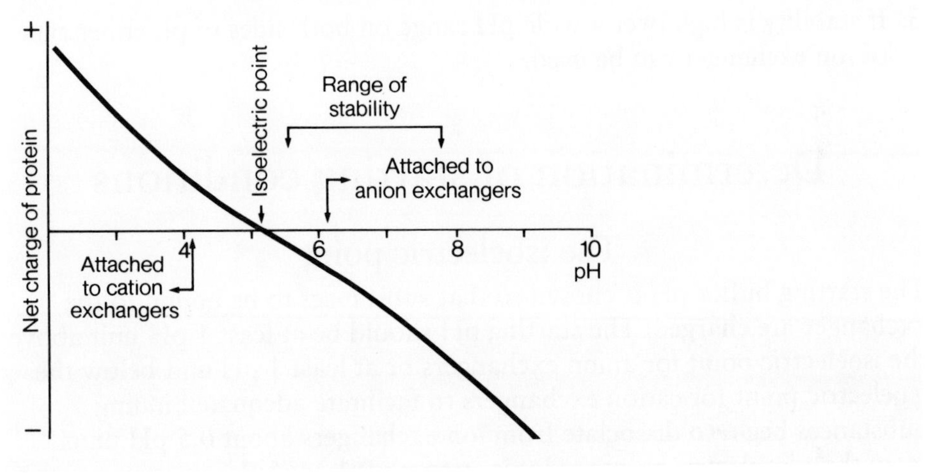

Fig. 24. The net charge of a protein as a function of pH.

The pH ranges in which the protein is bound to anion or cation exchangers and an arbitrary range of stability are shown.

The pH of the buffer thus determines the charge on amphoteric molecules during the experiment. In principle therefore, one could use either an anion or a cation exchanger to bind amphoteric samples by selecting the appropriate pH. In practice however, the choice is based on which exchanger type and pH give the best separation of the molecules of interest, within the constraints of their pH stability.

Methods for determining the optimum pH and corresponding ion exchanger type are discussed later in this chapter.

Many biological macromolecules become denatured or lose activity outside a certain pH range and thus the choice of ion exchanger may be limited by the stability of the sample. This is illustrated in Figure 24. Below its isoelectric point a protein has a net positive charge and therefore can adsorb to cation exchangers. Above its pl the protein has a net negative charge and can be adsorbed to anion exchangers. However, it is only stable in the range pH 5–8 and so an anion exchanger has to be used.

In summary:

1. If the sample components are most stable below their pI's, a cation exchanger should be used.
2. If they are most stable above their pI's, an anion exchanger should be used.
3. If stability is high over a wide pH range on both sides of pI, either type of ion exchanger can be used.

Determination of starting conditions

The isoelectric point

The starting buffer pH is chosen so that substances to be bound to the exchanger are charged. The starting pH should be at least 1 pH unit above the isoelectric point for anion exchangers or at least 1 pH unit below the isoelectric point for cation exchangers to facilitate adequate binding. Substances begin to dissociate from ion exchangers about 0.5 pH units from their isoelectric points at ionic strength 0.1 M (16).

There are comprehensive lists of isoelectric points determined for proteins (17, 18) which can be useful in the design of ion exchange experiments.

If the isoelectric point of the sample is unknown, a simple test can be performed to determine which starting pH can be used.

Test-tube method for selecting starting pH

1. Set up a series of 10 test-tubes (15 ml).
2. Add 0.1 g Sephadex ion exchanger or 1.5 ml Sepharose or Sephacel ion exchanger to each tube.
3. Equilibrate the gel in each tube to a different pH by washing 10 times with 10 ml of 0.5 M buffer (see page 61 for choice of buffers for ion

exchange). Use a range of pH 5–9 for anion and pH 4–8 for cation exchangers, with 0.5 pH unit intervals between tubes.

4. Equilibrate the gel in each tube at a lower ionic strength (0.05 M for Sephadex or 0.01 M for Sepharose and Sephacel ion exchangers) by washing 5 times with 10 ml of buffer of the same pH but lower ionic strength.
5. Add a known constant amount of sample to each tube.
6. Mix the contents of the tubes for 5–10 minutes.
7. Allow the gel to settle.
8. Assay the supernatant for the substance of interest. The results may appear as shown in Figure 25(a).

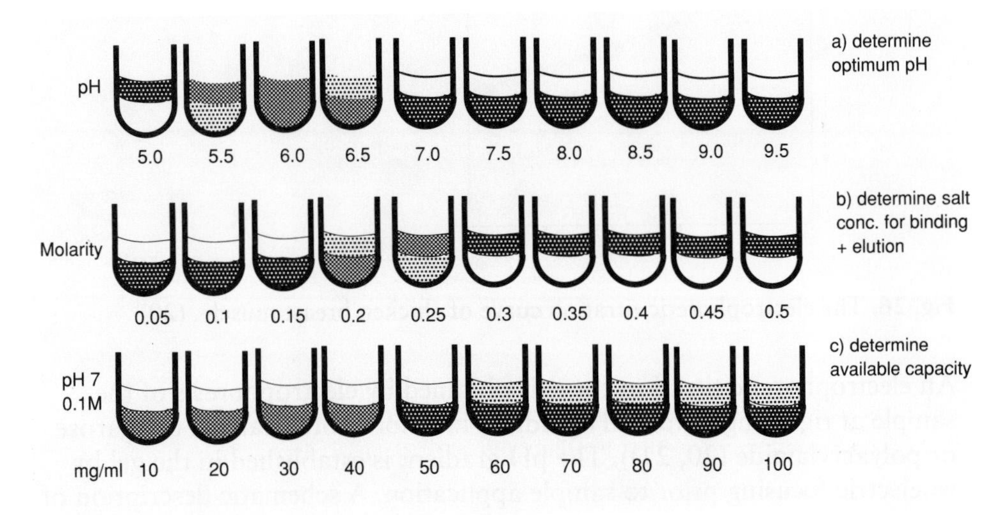

Fig. 25. Test-tube methods for selecting ion exchange conditions.

The pH to be used in the experiment should allow the substance to be bound, but should be as close to the point of release as possible. If too low (or high) a pH is chosen, elution may become more difficult and high salt concentrations may have to be used. In Figure 25 the buffer chosen should be pH 7.0.

Electrophoretic titration curves (ETC)

While information on the pI of the sample components gives valuable indications concerning the choice of starting conditions, it does not give a picture of how the charge on the molecules varies with pH (Fig. 24), nor indicate at what pH or on which exchanger type maximum resolution could be expected.

Electrophoretic titration curves (Fig. 26) enable the determination of the charge pH relationship for the molecules present across a continuum of pH and are a particularly useful way of predicting suitable conditions for an ion exchange separation (19).

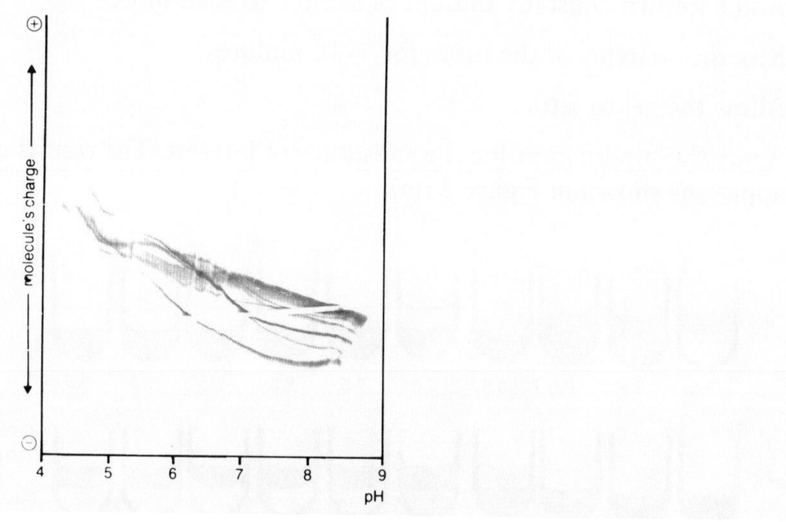

Fig. 26. The electrophoretic titration curve of chicken breast muscle. (20)

An electrophoretic titration curve is obtained by electrophoresis of the sample at right angles to a pH gradient in a horizontal slab gel of agarose or polyacrylamide (20, 21)). The pH gradient is established in the gel by isoelectric focusing prior to sample application. A schematic description of the various steps is shown in Fig. 27. A detailed description of the method using PhastSystem and Multiphor II electrophoresis systems is available upon request from Pharmacia LKB Biotechnology.

Electrophoresis of the sample perpendicular to the pH gradient produces a series of curves, unique for each component, since the relative electrophoretic mobility of each component will be different depending on its net charge at given pH values. The pH value where each curve intersects the line of sample application represents the pH at which that particular component has a zero net charge, the pI for that component.

Maximum resolution can be expected at a pH where there is maximum separation between the titration curves for individual solutes, using the ion

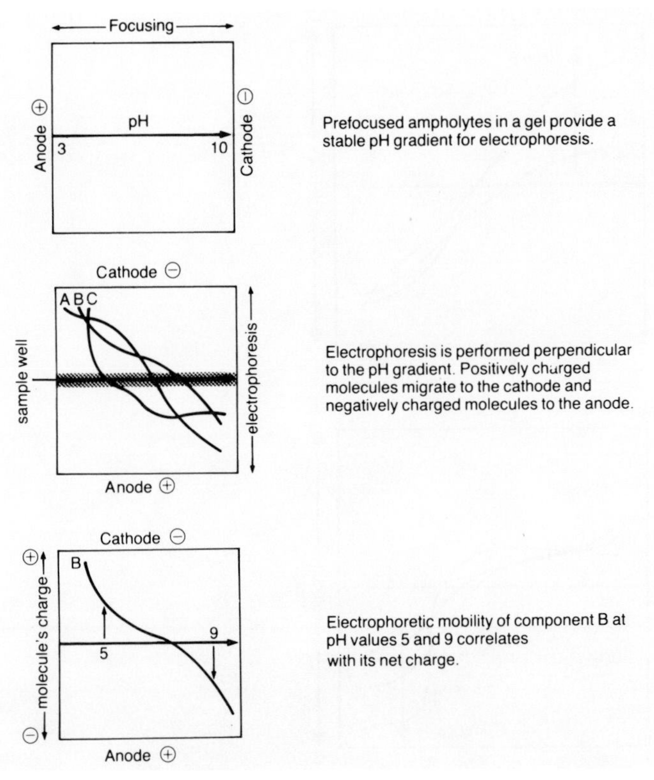

Fig. 27. The major steps in making electrophoretic titration curves.

exchanger type indicated by the charge of the molecules at that particular pH. At this pH the difference in electrophoretic mobilities and hence net charges between the species is greatest. This principle is illustrated in Fig. 28. The protein's stability at the indicated pH must be taken into consideration before applying these conditions to the separation.

If maximum separation is observed at a pH where the sample molecules are positively charged i.e. below their isoelectric points, maximum resolution will be obtained using a cation exchanger such as S Sepharose Fast Flow or Mono S.

If the largest difference in electrophoretic mobility is found at a pH where the components of interest are negatively charged i.e. above their isoelectric points, an anion exchanger such as Q Sepharose Fast Flow or Mono Q should be chosen.

If maximum separation of the curves occurs at the position of sample application i.e. at the isoelectric points of the molecules, then maximum

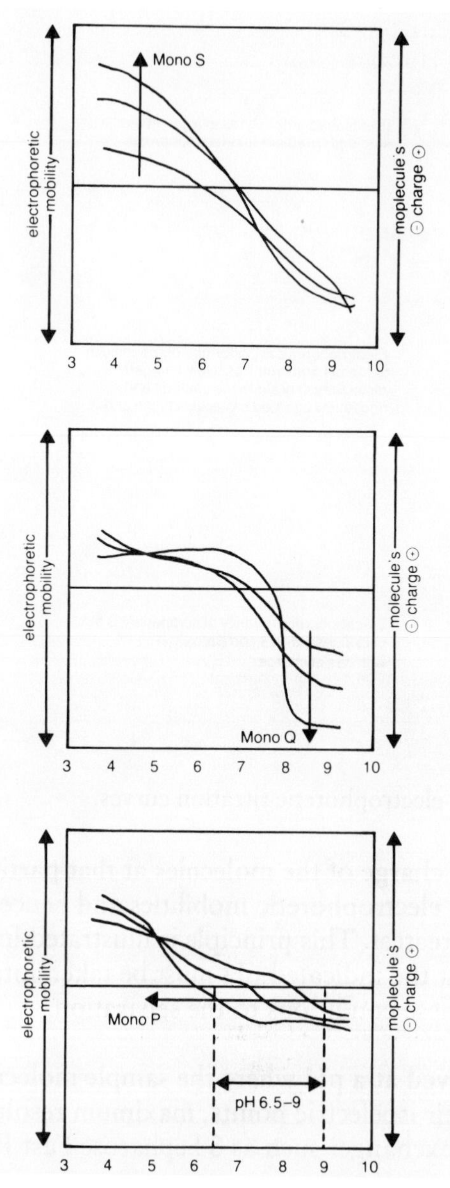

Fig. 28. Column selection based on electrophoretic titration curve analysis.

resolution may be achieved using the technique of chromatofocusing. Further information on techniques and media for chromatofocusing is available on request.

Measurement of pH can be done using a surface electrode or by running pI calibration proteins as a narrow band at the top or bottom of the slab gel during the first dimension electrophoresis as the pH gradient is established in the gel. This section of the gel is removed and stained before the sample is applied for the second dimension electrophoresis and then afterwards replaced to estimate pH values.

Staining the titration curve with a general protein stain such as Coomassie Blue does not give any information about the charge/pH relationship for specific proteins unless they can be clearly identified by their isoelectric points. To gain positive identification it is necessary to use a specific detection technique such as zymographic analysis or immunofixation as illustrated in Fig. 29.

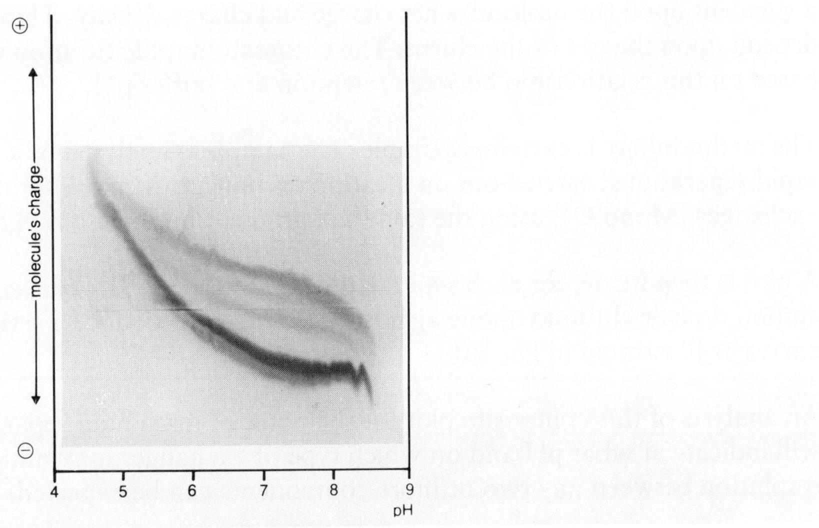

Fig. 29. The electrophoretic titration curve of chicken breast muscle using zymogram detection for creatine kinase (20).

In addition to information regarding optimal starting conditions, the electrophoretic titration curves also reveal important information which will assist the interpretation of the chromatogram after the run.

Since the lines on the ETC reflect the degree of charge of the components at different pH´s, the curves may be used to predict the order in which the components will be eluted from the column. The molecular species with the lowest electrophoretic mobility at a certain pH has logically the lowest charge at that particular pH and should be the first substance eluted from the column in the gradient. Similarly the species showing highest electrophoretic mobility will be the most strongly retained on a column of opposite charge and should be eluted last. The order in which solutes are eluted cannot be predicted with 100% certainty from the titration curve since electrophoretic mobility depends on the total net charge on a molecule and ion exchange chromatography depends on the net charge on the solutes surface.

Chromatographic titration curves (retention maps)

For those ion exchanger types which allow rapid separations, optimal starting pH and choice of anion or cation exchanger can be determined using chromatographic titration curves (19).

In a specified salt gradient, the retention of particular molecular species is dependent upon the molecules net charge and charge density. These in turn depend upon the pH of the eluent. The chromatographic titration curve is based on this relationship between retention and buffer pH.

The methodology is extremely simple. The sample is analysed in a series of rapid separations, carried out on a cation exchanger (Mono S) or an anion exchanger (Mono Q), using the same salt gradient but over a range of pH´s.

A plot is then made, for each separated peak, of elution salt concentration, elution time or elution volume against pH. This will produce a series of curves as illustrated in Fig. 30.

An analysis of this composite plot for the point of maximum separation will indicate at what pH and on which type of exchanger maximum resolution between any two or more components can be expected.

The conditions used (column type, buffers, pH, etc.) during the rapid runs for the generation of the chromatographic titration curves can be directly applied when developing the final optimized procedure.

Choice between strong and weak ion exchangers

Having selected a suitable starting pH to use on a cation or anion exchanger, it is necessary to choose between a strong and weak ion exchange group. In those cases where maximum resolution occurs at an extreme of pH and the molecules of interest are stable at that pH, the choice is clearly to use a strong exchanger. The majority of proteins however, have isoelectric points which lie within the range 5.5 to 7.5 and can thus be separated on both strong and weak ion exchangers. Some advantages in using a strong ion exchanger are discussed in Chapter 2.

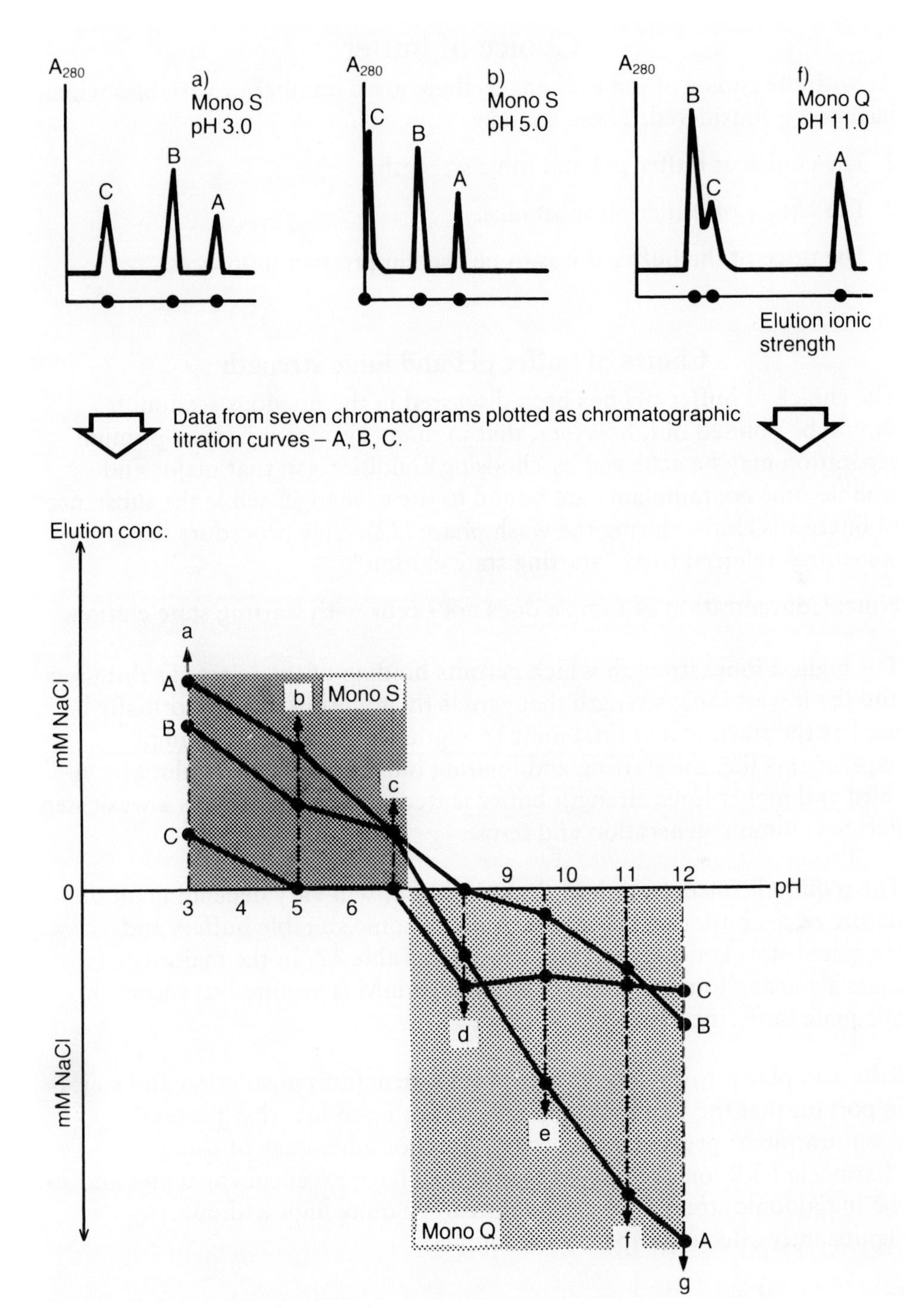

Fig. 30. Chromatographic titration curves.

Choice of buffer

As with the choice of ion exchanger, there are a number of variables which have to be considered. These include:

1. The choice of buffer pH and ionic strength.
2. The choice of buffering substance.
3. The price of the buffer if it is to be used in production process.

Choice of buffer pH and ionic strength

The choice of buffer pH has been discussed in the previous section. It should be pointed out, however, that in many applications the optimum separation may be achieved by choosing conditions so that major and troublesome contaminants are bound to the exchanger while the substance of interest is eluted during the wash phase (22). This procedure is sometimes referred to as "starting state elution".

Note: Concentration of sample does not occur with starting state elution.

The highest ionic strength which permits binding of the selected substances and the lowest ionic strength that causes their elution should normally be used as the starting and final ionic strengths in subsequent column experiments (i.e. the starting and limiting buffers for gradient elution). A third and higher ionic strength buffer is frequently employed as a wash step before column regeneration and re-use.

The required concentration of the start buffer will vary depending on the nature of the buffering substance. A list of some suitable buffers and suggested start concentrations is shown in Table 12. In the majority of cases a starting ionic strength of at least 10 mM is required to ensure adequate buffering capacity.

Salts also play a role in stabilizing protein structures in solution and so it is important that the ionic strength should not be so low that protein denaturation or precipitation occurs. A major advantage of using Pharmacia LKB ion exchangers is that they have excellent capacities and so the initial ionic strength of the buffer can be quite high without significantly affecting capacity for sample.

In the case of prepacked ion exchangers and columns which can be run conveniently quickly, trial experiments using salt gradients will allow the determination of an optimal starting ionic strength.

Table 12. Buffer tables.
Buffer substances for cation exchange chromatography

pKa (25°C)	pH interval	Substance	Conc. (mM)	dpKa/ dT (°C)	Counter-ion	Comments
2.00	1.5–2.5	Maleic acid	20		Na^+	Dicarboxylic acid
2.88	2.38–3.38	Malonic acid	20		Na^+/Li^+	Dicarboxylic acid
3.13	2.63–3.63	Citric acid	20	–0.0024	Na^+	Dicarboxylic acid
3.81	3.6–4.3	Lactic acid	50		Na^+	
*3.75	3.8–4.3	Formic acid	50	+0.0002	Na^+/Li^+	
*4.21	4.3–4.8	Butanedioic acid	50	–0.0018	Na^+	
*4.76	4.8–5.2	Acetic acid	50	+0.0002	Na^+/Li^+	
*5.68	5.0–6.0	Malonic acid	50		Na^+/Li^+	Dicarboxylic acid
*7.20	6.7–7.6	Phosphate	50	–0.0028	Na^+	Often needs purication before use
*7.55	7.6–8.2	HEPES	50	–0.0140	Na^+/Li^+	Zwitterionic
*8.35	8.2–8.7	BICINE	50	–0.0180	Na^+	Zwitterionic

Buffer substances for cation exchange chromatography

pKa (25°C)	pH interval	Substance	Conc. (mM)	dpKa/ dT (°C)	Counter-ion	Comments
*4.75	4.5–5.0	N-methyl piperazine	20	–0.015	$C1^-$	
*5.68	5.0–6.0	Piperazine	20	–0.015	$C1^-/HCOO^-$	
*5.96	5.5–6.0	L-histidine	20		$C1^-$	
*6.46	5.8–6.4	bis-Tris	20	–0.017	$C1^-$	
*6.80	6.4–7.3	bis-Tris propane	20		$C1^-$	
*7.76	7.3–7.7	Triethanolamine	20	–0.020	$C1^-/$ CH_3COO^-	
*8.06	7.6–8.0	Tris	20	–0.028	$C1^-$	Often needs purication before use and
*8.52	8.0–8.5	N-methyl-diethanolamine	50	–0.028	$SO^{2-}/C^-/$ CH_3COO^-	especially sensitive to temperature
*8.88	8.4–8.8	Diethanolamine	20 at 8.4 50 at 8.8	–0.025	$C1^-$	change.
*8.64	8.5–9.0	1,3-diamino-propane	20	–0.031	$C1^-$	
*9.50	9.0–9.5	Ethanolamine	20	–0.029	$C1^-$	
*9.73	9.5–9.8	Piperazine	20	–0.026	$C1^-$	
*10.47	9.8–10.3	1,3-diamino-propane	20	–0.026	$C1^-$	
11.12	10.6–11.6	Piperadine	20	–0.031	$C1^-$	
12.33	11.8–12.0	Phosphate	20	–0.026	$C1^-$	

* Recommended on the basis of experiments performed in our laboratories.

In the case of Sephadex based exchangers for batch applications or where column running times are prohibitively long, a simple test-tube technique is recommended as a test for a suitable ionic strength.

Test-tube method for selecting starting ionic strengths

1. Set up a series of tubes with ion exchanger as detailed on page 53.

2. Equilibrate the gel in each tube with 0.5 M buffer at the selected starting pH (10 x 10 ml washes).

3. Equilibrate the gel in each tube to a different ionic strength, at constant pH, using a range from 0.05 M to 0.5 M NaCl for Sephadex ion exchangers and from 0.01 M to 0.3 M NaCl for Sephacel and Sepharose ion exchangers. This will require 5 x 10 ml washes. Intervals of 0.05 M NaCl are sufficient.

4. Add sample, mix and assay the supernatant to determine the maximum ionic strength which permits binding of the substance of interest and the minimum ionic strength required for complete desorption.

In the hypothetical example shown in Figure 25(b) the ionic strength for sample binding (start buffer) would be at most 0.15 M and for elution at least 0.3 M.

Choice of buffer substance

If the buffering ions carry a charge opposite to that of the functional groups of the ion exchanger they will take part in the ion exchange process and cause local disturbances in pH. It is preferable, therefore, to use buffering ions with the same charge sign as the substituent groups on the ion exchanger. There are of course exceptions to this rule as illustrated by the frequency with which phosphate buffers are cited in the literature in connection with anion exchangers. In those instances when a buffering ion which interacts with the ionic groups on the matrix is used, extra care must be taken to ensure that the system has come to equilibrium before application of sample.

In cases where substances purified by ion exchange chromatography have to be freeze dried it is advantageous to use volatile buffer systems. Examples of such systems are shown in Table 13.

Table 13. Volatile buffer systems.

pH	Substance	Counter-ion
2.0	Formic acid	H^+
2.3–3.5	Pyridine/formic acid	$HCOO^-$
3.0–5.0	Trimethylamine/formic acid	$HCOO^-$
3.0–6.0	Pyridine/acetic acid	CH_3OO^-
4.0–6.0	Trimethylamine/acetic acid	CH_3COO^-
6.8-8.8	Trimethylamine/HC1	$C1^-$
7.0–8.5	Ammonia/formic acid	$HCOO^-$
8.5–10.0	Ammonia/acid	CH_3COO^-
7.0–12.0	Trimethylamine/CO2	CO_3^-
7.0–12.0	Triethylamine/CO2	CO_3^-
7.9	Ammonium bicarbonate	HCO_3^-
8.0–9.5	Ammonium carbonate/ammonia	CO_3^-
8.5–10.5	Ethanolamine/HC1	$C1^-$
8.9	Ammonium carbonate	CO_3^-

Preparation of the ion exchanger

Having chosen the appropriate ion exchanger and starting buffer it is essential that the exchanger is brought to equilibrium with start buffer before sample application. An advantage of all ion exchangers available from Pharmacia LKB is that they are supplied in salt form and do not require pre-cycling (i.e. treatment with acid and alkali) before equilibration. The procedure for equilibration for Sephadex ion exchangers, which are supplied as powders, differs somewhat from that of Sephacel, Sepharose and MonoBeads based ion exchangers which are supplied pre-swollen and/ or prepacked.

Sephadex ion exchangers

Sephadex ion exchangers should be swollen at the pH to be used in the experiment. Complete swelling takes 1–2 days at room temperature or 2 hours (at pH 7) in a boiling water bath. Swelling at high temperature also serves to de-aerate the gel. Vigorous stirring (e.g. with a magnetic stirrer) and swelling in distilled water should be avoided due to the risk of damaging the beads.

The required amount of ion exchanger should be stirred into an excess of starting buffer. The starting buffer must contain the same ion as that originally present in the ion exchanger. Remove the supernatant and replace with fresh buffer several times during the swelling period. Instead of decantation, the ion exchanger can be washed extensively on a Buchner funnel after the initial swelling.

Pre-Swollen ion exchangers

Sepharose Fast Flow, Sepharose CL-6B and DEAE Sephacel ion exchange media are supplied ready to use. To prepare the gel, the supernatant is decanted and replaced with starting buffer to a ratio of approximately 75% settled gel : 25% buffer.

If large amounts of ion exchanger are to be equilibrated with a weak buffer, the ion exchanger should first be equilibrated with a 10 times concentrated solution of start buffer at the correct pH, and then with a few volumes of starting buffer.

Sepharose High Performance and MonoBeads

Sepharose High Performance and MonoBeads based ion exchangers are supplied prepacked and ready to use in HiLoad and HR columns respectively. Column preparation consists of washing out the 25% ethanol packing solution with 5 column volumes of start buffer.

Alternative counter-ions

If ion exchangers are to be used with counter-ions other than those supplied (i.e. other than sodium or chloride) then the following procedure should be used.

Suspend the required amount of ion exchanger in an excess of 0.5–1.0 M solution of a salt of the new counter-ion. After sedimentation and decantation, re-suspend the ion exchanger in the buffer to be used in the experiment. Decant and re-suspend the ion exchanger in this buffer several times.

Decantation of fines

Decantation of fines is not necessary with any Pharmacia LKB Biotechnology ion exchangers.

Quantity of ion exchanger

The amount of ion exchanger required for a given experiment depends on the amount of sample to be chromatographed and on the available or dynamic capacity of the ion exchanger for the sample substances. For the best resolution in ion exchange chromatography, it is not usually advisable to use more than 10–20% of this capacity, although this value can be exceeded if resolution is adequate.

The available capacity of the ion exchanger can be determined using the methods outlined in Chapter 9.

9. Experimental Technique II

Column chromatography

There are two ways of performing an ion exchange separation: by batch methods or by column chromatography. This section will mostly deal with column chromatography.

Choice of column

Good results in column chromatography are not solely dependent on the correct choice of gel media. The design of the column and good packing technique are also important in realising the full separation potential of any gel. These factors are built into the prepacked columns supplied by Pharmacia LKB Biotechnology and should be considered before packing a chromatography column in the laboratory.

Column design

The material used in the construction of the column should be chosen to prevent destruction of labile biological substances. The bed support should be designed so that clogging by biological materials or gel particles does not occur. Bed supports made from coarse sintered glass or glass wool cannot be recommended because they soon become clogged, are difficult to clean and cause artifacts (23). Dead spaces must be kept to a minimum to prevent re-mixing of separated zones.

Pharmacia has developed a series of standard columns suitable for ion exchange chromatography. Their design is based on many years of experience in gel filtration and ion exchange. They are manufactured from materials which do not cause destruction of labile biological substances. All are easy to dismantle and re-assemble to allow thorough cleaning, which is a particularly important aspect when handling biological samples.

Other important characteristics of Pharmacia laboratory columns include:

- Dead space at the outlet of less than 0.1% of the column volume. Minimizes dilution and prevents re-mixing of separated zones.
- Advanced design bed supports which give uniform flow with minimal clogging.

- All columns normally used for ion exchange chromatography can be fitted with flow adaptors for easy sample application and reproducible separations.

Further information on the full range of Pharmacia chromatography columns can be found in "Standard Chromatography Instrument and System Guide" which is available upon request.

Larger chromatography columns, specially designed for pilot and process scale chromatography are also available. Further information on these columns can be found in "Column Selection Guide"

Column height

Conditions should be chosen such that the sample substances are adsorbed within the upper 1 to 2 cm of the ion exchanger bed. Ion exchange chromatography is normally carried out in short columns if gradient elution is employed. For the majority of separations a bed height which is not more than four times the column diameter can be recommended. A bed height of 10 cm is often sufficient (24). Longer beds may be necessary for resolution of very complex mixtures. However, care should be exercised when using longer columns for ion exchange since diffusion in longer columns may have the effect of reducing the resolution.

Column diameter

If the bed height is fixed, the column diameter required can be calculated on the basis of how much ion exchanger is required. e.g. If 100 ml of gel is required and the bed height is 20 cm then a column with a 2.6 cm diameter should be used. Ion exchange chromatography is usually run on short broad columns with scale-up achieved by using broader columns of the same length.

Packing the column

As with any other chromatographic technique, packing is a very critical stage in an ion exchange experiment. A poorly packed column gives rise to poor and uneven flow, zone broadening, and loss of resolution. Packing an ion exchange column, particularly with the modern media such as Sepharose Fast Flow, is easier than packing a gel filtration column since the bed height required is usually much smaller.

Column Packing Video Film

A video film describing the correct methodologies for packing laboratory columns is available and can be ordered from your local distributor of Pharmacia LKB Biotechnology products.

Sephadex ion exchangers

Filling the column

1. The swollen ion exchanger should be mixed with starting buffer so that it forms a slurry which is fairly thick but not so thick as to retain air bubbles. Normally about 75% settled gel is suitable. Unless the gel has been swollen on a boiling water bath, it should be degassed under vacuum. The gel should be at the temperature of column operation before packing is begun.

2. Mount the column vertically on a suitable stand out of direct sunlight or draughts which can cause temperature fluctuations.

3. Using a syringe, eliminate air from the column dead spaces by flushing the end pieces with buffer. Make sure no air has been trapped under the bed net. Close the column outlet.

4. Pour the ion exchanger suspension into the column either down a glass rod or down the side of the chromatographic tube to avoid bubble formation. The use of a gel and eluent reservoir enables all the ion exchanger suspension to be poured at one time.

5. Open the column outlet and allow the gel to settle into the column. When all the suspension has run into the column the reservoir can be removed and the top piece connected to the column. If the suspension does not fill the column, starting buffer should be carefully added until the level is 1 cm from the top of the column before connecting the top piece. The column should then be connected to a buffer reservoir containing degassed buffer. Any air remaining in the column can be removed by opening the air vent in the column top piece.

6. Close the air vent. The column outlet should be opened as soon as possible to maintain an even rate of sedimentation during packing.

Note: The packing buffer should not contain agents which significantly increase viscosity (e.g. glycerol). The gel may be equilibrated with viscous buffers at reduced flow rates after packing.

Packing and equilibrating the bed

1. Adjust the column outlet so that the operating pressure is equivalent to about 1 cm H_2O per cm height of gel bed.

2. Allow the ion exchanger to pack under constant pressure, using for example a mariott flask. The flow rate should be at least 133% of that to be used during subsequent separations, to allow for viscosity and consequent pressure differences due to sample application.

3. Run at least two bed volumes of buffer through the ion exchange bed in order to allow the system to reach equilibrium and to stabilize the bed. Counter-ion concentration, conductivity, and pH of the eluent should be checked against the ingoing solution, but it is often sufficient just to measure the pH of the effluent as a check that equilibration is complete.

Checking the packing

The bed should be inspected for irregularities or air bubbles using transmitted light from a lamp held behind the column. Be careful in the choice of any dye substances used for checking beds as many of them are strongly charged. For example, Blue Dextran 2000 binds strongly to anion exchangers.

After packing, the bed can be fitted with a flow adaptor if desired. This is less suitable for Sephadex A-50 and C-50 ion exchangers, which may change in volume during elution, but an adaptor can be used to protect the bed surface with the other types of ion exchanger. Alternatively, layer about 0.5 cm Sephadex G-25 Coarse (swollen in the same buffer as the ion exchanger) onto the top of the bed to act as a bed surface protectant.

Sepharose CL-6B based ion exchangers

Filling the column

1. The pre-swollen ion exchanger should be mixed with starting buffer so that it forms a slurry which is fairly thick but not so thick as to retain air bubbles. Usually about 75% settled gel and 25% buffer is suitable. The gel should be degassed under vacuum and at the temperature of column operation before packing is begun.

Note: The packing buffer should not contain agents which significantly increase viscosity (e.g. glycerol). The gel may be equilibrated with viscous buffers at reduced flow rates after packing.

2. Mount the column vertically on a suitable stand out of direct sunlight or draughts which can cause temperature fluctuations.

3. Eliminate air from the column dead spaces by flushing the end pieces with buffer. Make sure no air has been trapped under the column net. Close the column outlet with a few centimeters of buffer remaining in the column.

4. Pour the ion exchanger suspension into the column either down a glass rod or down the side of the chromatographic tube to avoid bubble formation.

5. Immediately fill the remainder of the column with buffer, fit the top-piece to the column, using the vent to exclude air bubbles and connect the column to a pump.

Packing the bed

Open the outlet at the bottom of the column and establish the required flow rate. This should be at least 133% of the flow rate to be used during subsequent chromatographic procedures. However, the maximum flow rate is typically employed during packing. The packing flow rate is maintained until a constant bed height has been reached.

Checking the packing

The bed should be inspected for irregularities or air bubbles using transmitted light from a lamp held behind the column. Be careful in the choice of any dye substances used for checking beds as many of them are strongly charged. For example, Blue Dextran 2000 binds strongly to anion exchangers.

Use of an adaptor

Adaptors are adjustable column end pieces which allow optimal sample injection, eliminate disturbance of the bed surface and protect the bed from insoluble particles in the sample. They can also be used as the column bottom piece to give increased flexibility in the choice of bed height.

Adaptors should be fitted as follows:

1. After the gel has been packed as described above, close the column outlet and remove the top piece from the column. Carefully add more buffer into the column to form an upward meniscus.

2. Slacken the adaptor tightening mechanism and insert the adaptor at an angle into the column, ensuring that no air is trapped under the net.

3. Adjust the tightening mechanism to give a sliding seal between the column wall and the O-ring. Screw the adaptor end piece on to the column.

4. Make all tubing connections at this stage. There must be a bubble-free liquid connection between the column and the pump and the column and the sample application system. (LV-3 or LV-4).

5. Slide the plunger slowly down the column so that the air above the net and in the capillary tubings is displaced by eluent. Valves on the inlet side of the column should be turned in all directions during this procedure to ensure that air is removed

6. Lock the adaptor in position with the tightening mechanism and the locking screw or clip, open the column outlet and start the eluent flow. Pass eluent through the column at the packing flow rate until the gel bed is stable, re-positioning the adaptor on the gel surface as necessary.

Equilibrating the bed

Run at least two bed volumes of buffer through the ion exchange bed to allow the system to reach equilibrium. Counter-ion concentration, conductivity, and pH of the eluent should be checked against the ingoing solution. It is often sufficient just to measure the pH of the effluent.

DEAE Sephacel

The packing procedure described above for Sepharose CL-6B ion exchangers can also be used with DEAE Sephacel.

Sepharose Fast Flow Gels

Sepharose Fast Flow ion exchangers are packed using a procedure identical to that for Sepharose CL-6B based media. Ideally Fast Flow media are packed at a constant pressure of 0.3 MPa (3 bar) for 5 cm diameter columns and 0.2 MPa (2 bar) for column diameters of 1.6 and 2.6 cm. For peristaltic pumps, use the maximum flow which can be obtained if the maximum pressures are not possible.

Packing instructions for ion exchange media in BioPilot and BioProcess columns are are given in the detailed instruction manual which accompanies each column.

Prepacked ion exchange media

Sepharose Fast Flow, Sepharose High Performance and MonoBeads based ion exchangers are available in prepacked HiLoad and HR columns.

After connection of the column to the sample application system and detector, column preparation simply consists of washing out the 20% ethanol packing solution with start buffer and bringing the column to equilibrium.

Details on the installation and use of these columns is available in their respective instruction manuals.

Sample Preparation

Sample concentration

The amount of sample which can be applied to a column depends on the dynamic capacity of the column and the degree of resolution required. For the best resolution it is not usually advisable to use more than 10-20% of this capacity. Information on the available capacities for the different exchangers is given in the relevant product sections. Methods for determining available and dynamic capacities are given later.

Sample composition

The ionic composition should be the same as that of the starting buffer. If it is not, it can be changed by gel filtration on Sephadex G-25 using the Pharmacia Disposable Column PD-10, the FPLC Fast Desalting Column, dialysis, diafiltration or possibly by addition of concentrated start buffer.

Sample volume

If the ion exchanger is to be developed with the starting buffer (isocratic elution), the sample volume is important and should be limited to between 1 and 5% of the bed volume. If however, the ion exchanger is to be developed with a gradient, starting conditions are normally chosen so that all important substances are adsorbed at the top of the bed. In this case, the sample mass applied is of far greater importance than the sample volume. This means that large volumes of dilute solutions, such as pooled fractions from a preceding gel filtration step or a cell culture supernatant can be applied directly to the ion exchanger without prior concentration. Ion exchange thus serves as a useful means of concentrating a sample in addition to fractionating it.

If contaminants are to be adsorbed, and the component of interest is allowed to pass straight through, then the sample volume is less important than the amount of contaminant which is present. Under these conditions there will be no concentration of the purified component, rather some degree of dilution due to diffusion.

Sample viscosity

The viscosity may limit the quantity of sample that can be applied to a column. A high sample viscosity causes instability of the zone and an irregular flow pattern. The critical variable is the viscosity of the sample relative to the eluent. A rule of thumb is to use 4 cP as the maximum sample viscosity. This corresponds to a protein concentration of approximately 5%. Approximate relative viscosities can be quickly estimated by comparing emptying times from a pipette.

If the sample is too viscous, due to high solute concentration, it can be diluted with start buffer. High viscosity due to nucleic acid contaminants can be alleviated by precipitation or enzymic digest.

Sample Preparation

In all forms of chromatography good resolution and long column life depend on the sample being free from particulate matter. It is important that "dirty" samples are cleaned by filtration or centrifugation before being applied to the column.This requirement is particularly crucial when working with small particle matrices such as MonoBeads.

The "grade" of filter required for sample preparation depends on the particle size of the ion exchange matrix which will be used. Samples which are to be separated on a 90 µm medium can be filtered using a 1 µm filter. For 34 µm and 10 µm media, samples should be filtered through a 0.45 µm filter. When sterile filtration or extra clean samples are required, a 0.22 µm filter is appropriate.

Samples should be clear after filtration and free from visible contamination by lipids. If turbid solutions are injected onto the column, the column lifetime, resolution and capacity can be reduced. Centrifugation at 10 000 g for 15 minutes can also be used to prepare samples. This is not the ideal method of sample preparation but it is sometimes necessary if samples are of very small volume or adsorb non-specifically to filters.

Note: The latter may indicate that the substance in question may also adsorb strongly to chromatography matrices. Care should therefore be exercised and perhaps a buffer additive such as glycerol or a detergent used.

Crude samples containing lipids, salts, etc. can be passed through a suitably sized column of Sephadex G-25 e.g. Fast Desalting Column. Preliminary sample clean-up can be achieved simultaneously in this way .

Sample application

There are a number of ways to apply the sample.

Sample application with an adaptor

This is the recommended method for all ion exchange media with the exception of Sephadex based media and is always the method used with prepacked columns or when upward elution is employed. The sample may be presented to the column via the adaptor in one of the following ways.

Syringe method (Fig. 31). The valves LV-3 and LV-4 can be used as syringe holders to give a very simple method for the application of small samples in standard chromatography. Using this method the sample is allowed to run onto the column under gravity.

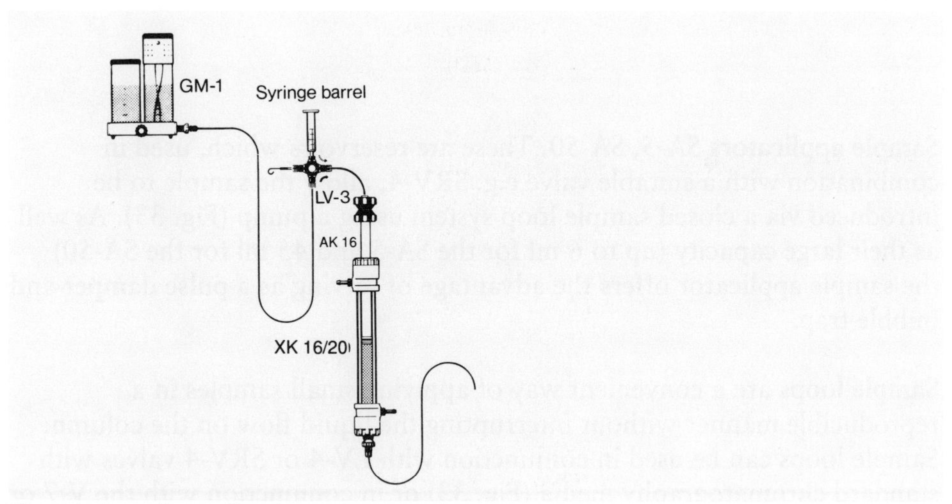

Fig. 31. Sample application using a syringe.

Sample reservoir (Fig. 32). In a similar way, a sample reservoir (e.g. R9, RK15/16) can be connected via a 3-way valve to apply larger samples.

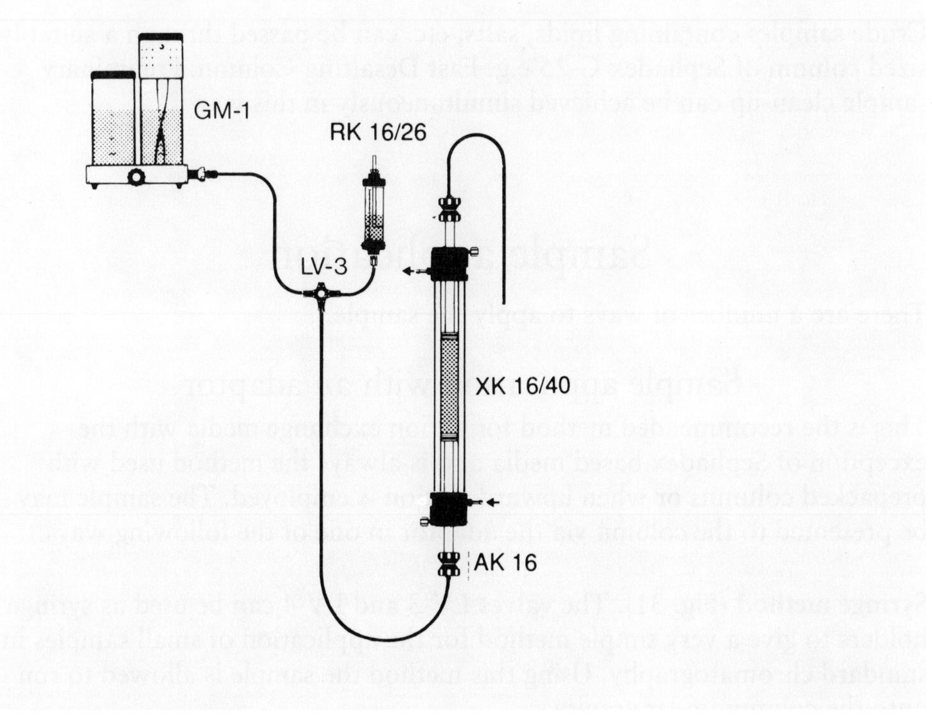

Fig. 32. Sample application using a reservoir. This is also an example of upward elution.

Sample applicators SA-5, SA-50. These are reservoirs which, used in combination with a suitable valve e.g. SRV-4, allow the sample to be introduced via a closed sample loop system using a pump (Fig. 33). As well as their large capacity (up to 6 ml for the SA-5 and 45 ml for the SA-50) the sample applicator offers the advantage of serving as a pulse damper and bubble trap.

Sample loops are a convenient way of applying small samples in a reproducible manner without interrupting the liquid flow on the column. Sample loops can be used in conjunction with LV-4 or SRV-4 valves with standard chromatography media (Fig. 33) or in conjunction with the V-7 or motorized MV-7 valves for high performance media (Fig. 34).

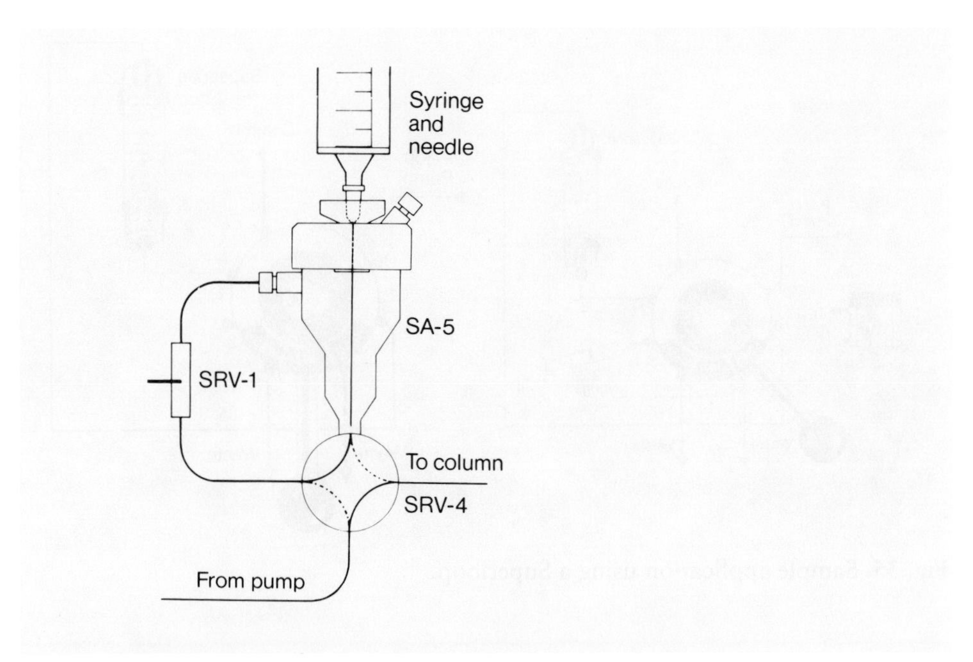

Fig. 33. Sample application using an SA-5 in a sample loop system.

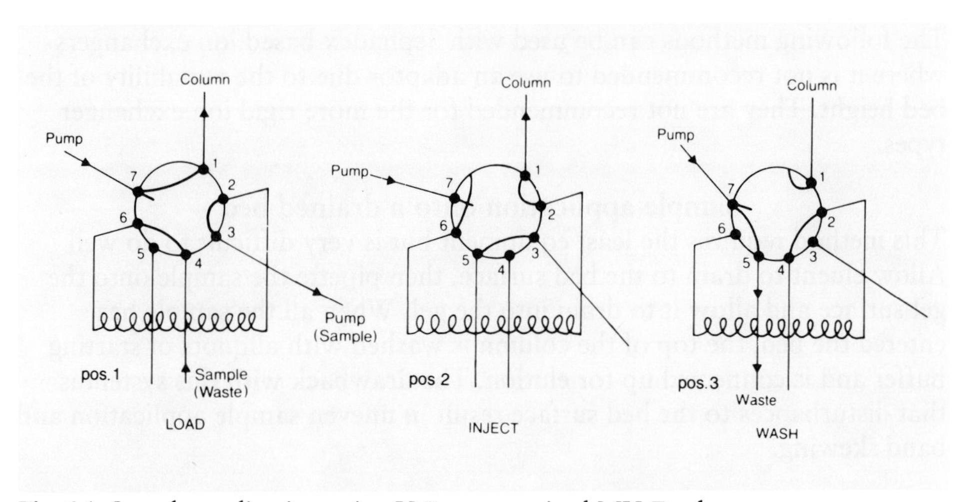

Fig. 34. Sample application using V-7 or motorized MV-7 valves.

Superloops can be used together with the V-7 or motorised MV-7 valves when larger volumes of sample have to be applied (Fig. 35). Superloops are available with capacities of up to 10 and 50 ml.

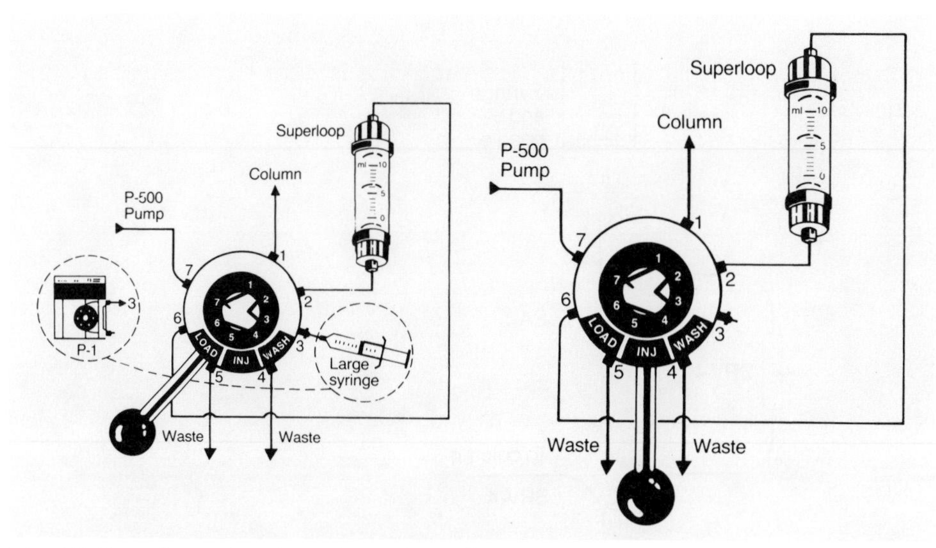

Fig. 35. Sample application using a Superloop.

Other methods of sample application

The following methods can be used with Sephadex based ion exchangers where it is not recommended to use an adaptor due to the variability of the bed height. They are not recommended for the more rigid ion exchanger types.

Sample application onto a drained bed

This method requires the least equipment but is very difficult to do well. Allow eluent to drain to the bed surface, then pipette the sample onto the gel surface and allow it to drain into the gel. When all the sample has entered the bed, the top of the column is washed with aliquots of starting buffer and is connected up for elution. The drawback with this system is that disturbances to the bed surface result in uneven sample application and band skewing.

Sample application under the eluent

Here excess eluent is left on top of the column. Some very thin capillary tubing is attached to a syringe and the free end is flared by gentle heating. The syringe is filled with sample which is then layered on top of the bed by positioning the end of the tubing just above the surface and slowly pressing out the sample. Note that the sample must be denser than the eluent or made denser by the addition of a sugar e.g. glucose (25). The column can then be connected for elution.

Elution

If starting conditions are chosen such that only unwanted substances in the sample are adsorbed, then no change in elution conditions is required since the substance of interest passes straight through the column. Similarly no changes are required if sample components are differentially retarded and separated under starting conditions. This procedure is termed isocratic elution, and the column is said to be developed under starting conditions. Isocratic elution can be useful since no gradient apparatus is required for the run and, if all retarded substances elute, regeneration is not required.

Normally, however, separation and elution are achieved by selectively decreasing the affinity of the solute molecules for the charged groups on the gel through changing either buffer pH or ionic strength or possibly both. This procedure is termed gradient elution.

Change of pH

As shown in Figure 24, the net charge on a molecule depends on pH. Thus altering the pH towards the isoelectric point of a substance causes it to lose its net charge, desorb, and elute from the ion exchanger. Figure 36 shows use of a decreasing pH gradient in separation of haemocyanin fractions (26).

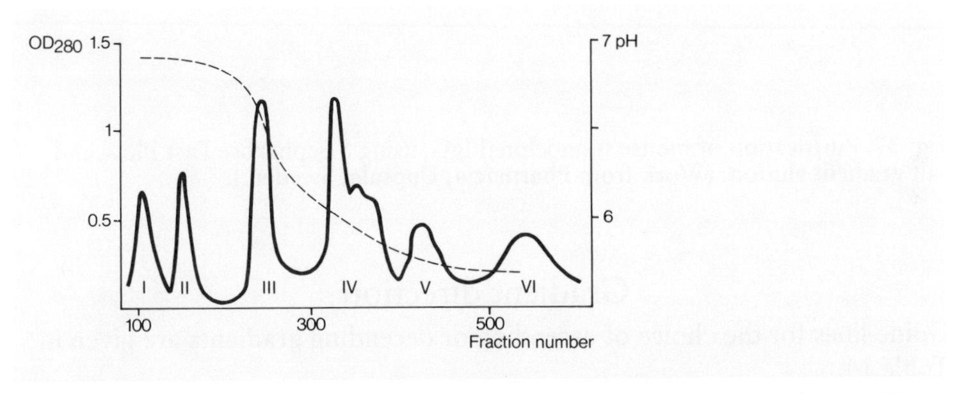

Fig. 36. Elution pattern of whole stripped haemocyanin on DEAE Sepharose CL-6B. Sample applied in 0.1 M sodium phosphate buffer pH 6.8 and eluted with decreasing pH gradient. (Lamy, J., Lamy, J., Weill, J. Arch. Biochem. Biophys. 193 (1979) 140-149. Reproduced by kind permission of the authors and publisher).

Since many proteins show minimum solubility in the vicinity of their isoelectric points, care and precautions must be exercised to avoid isoelectric precipitation on the column. The solubility of the sample components at the pH and salt concentrations to be used during separation should always be tested in advance.

Change of ionic strength

At low ionic strengths, competition for charged groups on the ion exchanger is at a minimum and substances are bound strongly. Increasing the ionic strength increases competition and reduces the interaction between the ion exchanger and the sample substances, resulting in their elution. Figure 37 shows the elution of monoclonal IgG on S Sepharose Fast Flow using a concentration gradient of NaCl.

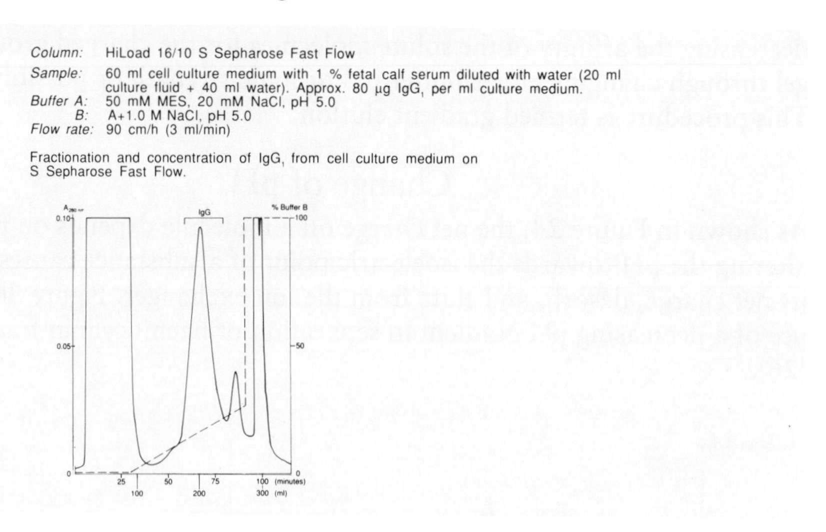

Fig. 37. Purification of mouse monoclonal IgG_1 using S Sepharose Fast Flow and salt gradient elution. (Work from Pharmacia, Uppsala, Sweden.).

Gradient direction

Guide-lines for the choice of ascending or decending gradients are given in Table 14.

Table 14. Choosing the direction of the gradient for elution.

Ion exchanger	Direction of pH gradient	Direction of ionic strength gradient
Anion exchanger	decreasing	increasing
Cation exchanger	increasing	increasing

Choice of gradient type

The components in the sample usually have different affinities for the ion exchanger and so variations in the pH and ionic strength of the eluent can cause their elution at different times and thus their separation from each other. One can choose to use either continuous or stepwise gradients of pH or ionic strength.

Stepwise pH gradients are easier to produce and are more reproducible than linear pH gradients. In the case of weak ion exchangers the buffer may have to titrate the ion exchanger and there will be a short period of re-equilibration before the new pH is reached. Gradients of pH can be also used in combination with ionic strength gradients.

Stepwise ionic strength gradients are produced by the sequential use of the same buffer at different ionic strengths. Stepwise elution is technically simple and offers the potential of high resolution in preparative applications. Care must be exercised in the design of the steps and the interpretation of results since substances eluted by a sharp change in pH or ionic strength elute close together. Peaks tend to have sharp fronts and pronounced tailing since they frequently contain more than one component. Tailing may lead to the appearance of false peaks if a buffer

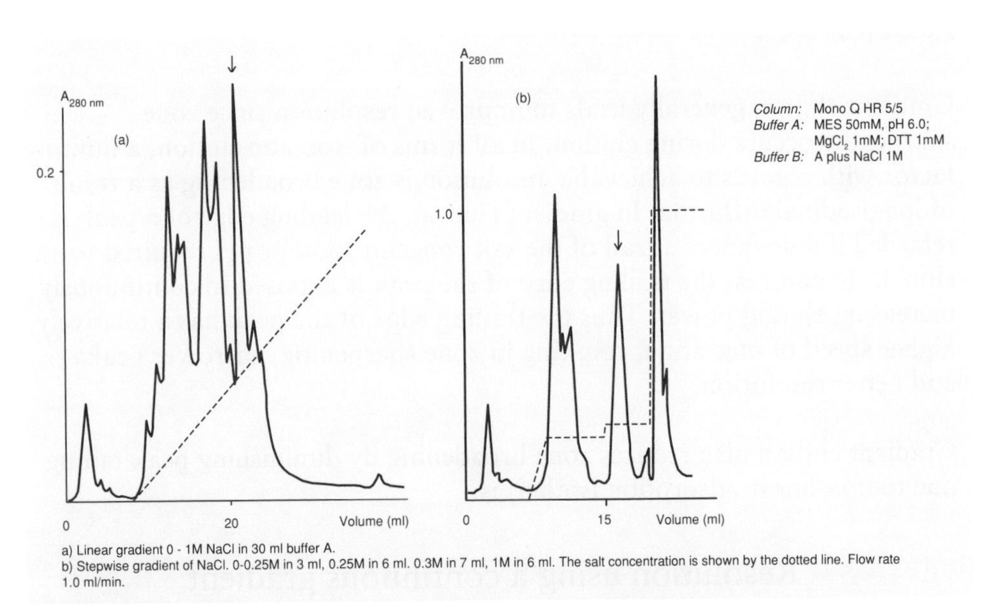

Fig. 38. Continuous and stepwise gradient elution of β-galactosidase from *Escherichia coli* on Mono Q HR 5/5 (27). Reproduced by kind permission of the authors and publisher.

change is introduced too early. For these reasons a first separation using a continuous gradient is always recommended as a means of characterising the sample and an indication of suitable steps. The differences between continuous and stepwise gradient elution are shown in Figure 38.

Continuous pH gradients are difficult to produce at constant ionic strength, since simultaneous changes in ionic strength, although small, also occur. Linear pH gradients cannot be obtained simply by mixing buffers of different pH in linear volume ratios since the buffering capacities of the systems produced are pH dependent. A relatively linear gradient can be produced over a narrow pH interval (Max. 2 pH units) by mixing two solutions of the same buffer salt adjusted, respectively, to 1 pH unit above and 1 pH unit below the pK_a for the buffer.

Continuous ionic strength gradients are the most frequently used type of elution in ion exchange chromatography. They are easy to prepare and very reproducible. Two buffers of differing ionic strength, the start and limit buffers, are mixed together and if the volume ratio is changed linearly, the ionic strength changes linearly.

The limit buffer may be of the same buffer salt and pH as the start buffer, but at higher concentration, or the start buffer containing additional salt e.g. NaCl.

Gradient elution generally leads to improved resolution since zone sharpening occurs during elution. In all forms of isocratic elution, a limiting factor with regards to achievable resolution is zone broadening as a result of longitudinal diffusion. In gradient elution, the leading edge of a peak is retarded if it advances ahead of the salt concentration or pH required to elute it. In contrast the trailing edge of the peak is exposed to continuously increasing eluting power. Thus the trailing edge of the peak has a relatively higher speed of migration, resulting in zone sharpening, narrower peaks and better resolution.

Gradient elution also reduces zone broadening by diminishing peak tailing due to non-linear adsorption isotherms.

Resolution using a continuous gradient

In order to optimize a separation it is important first to consider the objectives of the experiment, since the desired features of a separation i.e. speed, resolution and capacity, are often mutually exclusive.

In the case of ion exchange separations the speed of separation is not solely related to the flow rate used in the experiment but also to the steepness or slope of the gradient applied.

Novotny (28) has shown that the retention of charged molecules on an ion exchange column is related to the volume of the column and the molarity difference across it. This means that long shallow gradients will give maximum separation between peaks but that the separation time will be longer and peak broadening larger. In contrast short steep gradients will give faster separations and sharper peaks but the retention differences between peaks will be reduced. The effect of gradient slope on resolution is illustrated in Fig 39.

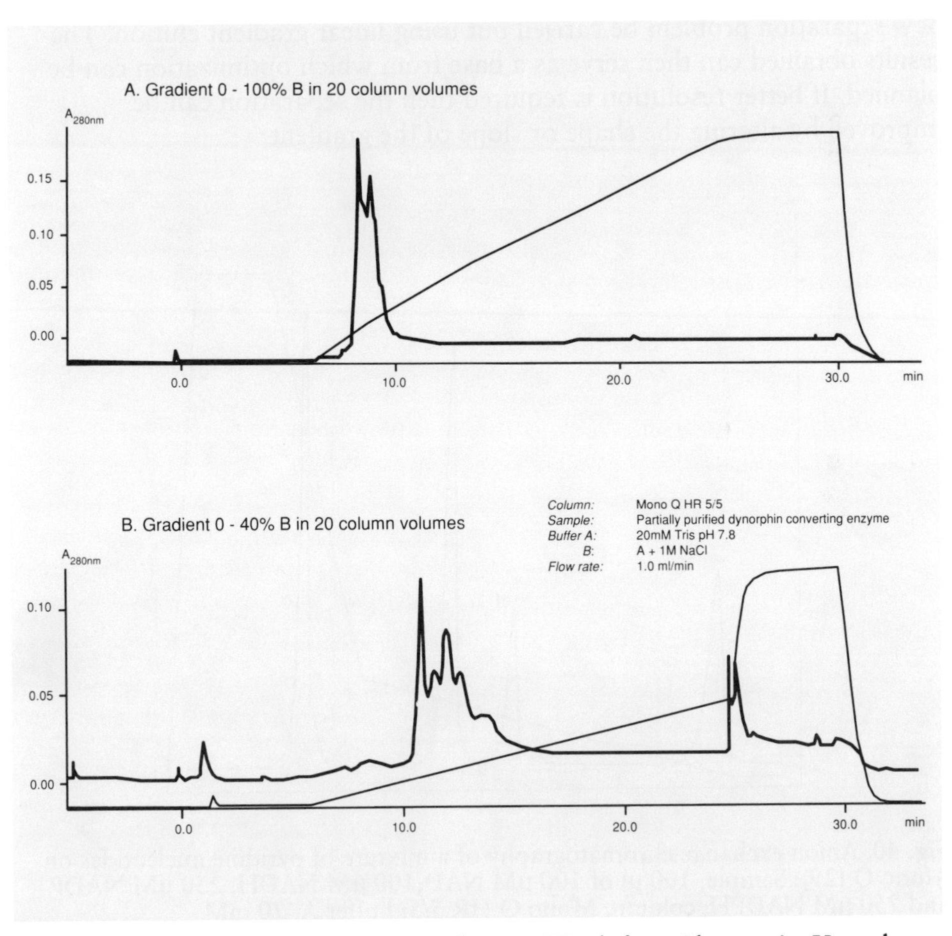

Fig. 39. Effect of gradient slope on resolution. (Work from Pharmacia, Uppsala, Sweden.).

It should be remembered that the sample loading also has a major influence on resolution since the width of the peaks is directly related to the amount of substance present.

In practice it is recommended that trial experiments be carried out to allow the selection of optimal run parameters in terms of gradient shape and length.

As a general rule a gradient of 0.05 to 0.5M salt over a volume of 10 to 20 column volumes at the flow rate recommended for the medium (See individual media sections) can be used for initial investigative separations.

Choice of gradient shape

Linear Gradients It is strongly recommended that initial experiments with a new separation problem be carried out using linear gradient elution. The results obtained can then serve as a base from which optimization can be planned. If better resolution is required then the separation can be improved by altering the shape or slope of the gradient.

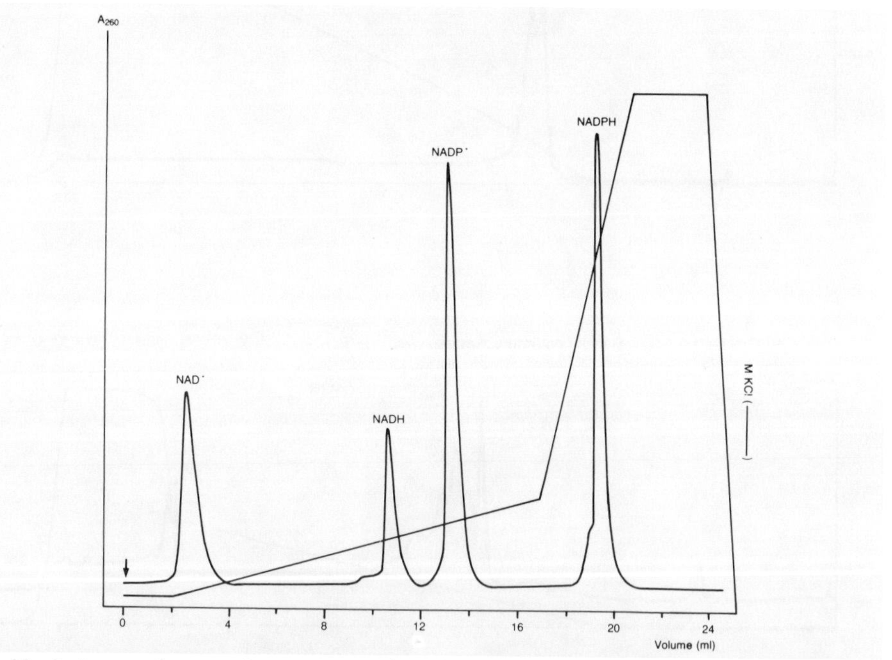

Fig. 40. Anion exchange chromatography of a mixture of pyridine nucleotides on Mono Q (29): Sample, 100 µl of 100 µM NAD,100 µM NADH, 250 µM NADP and 250 µM NADPH; column, Mono Q HR 5/5; buffer A, 20 mM triethanolamine, pH 7.7; buffer B, buffer A with 1.0 M KCl; gradient, 0% B for 2 ml, 0–20% B in 15 ml, 20-100% B in 5ml, 100% B for 3 ml; flow rate, 1 ml/min.

Convex gradients can be used to improve resolution in the last part of the gradient or to speed up a separation when the first peaks are well separated and the last few are adequately separated.

Concave gradients can be used to improve resolution in the first part of the gradient or to shorten the separation time when peaks in the latter part of the gradient are more than adequately separated.

Complex gradients can be generated to use the maximum resolution offered by isocratic resolution when required combined with steeper gradient portions where resolution is adequate or unnecessary (Fig. 40) Complex gradients offer the maximum flexibility in terms of combining resolution with speed during the same separation. A knowledge of the chromatographic behaviour of the sample obtained from previous separations using simpler gradients is essential.

Sample displacement

When a sample of solutes, such as proteins, is applied to the top of an ion exchange column the species with the highest charge density will bind at the top, displacing more weakly bound species or preventing such from binding.

In effect a degree of separation occurs on the column during sample loading, with the solutes stacked on the column in order of their relative charges and strengths of binding.

On application of a gradient the increasing salt concentration will cause the most weakly bound molecules to migrate and leave the column first. For this reason "reverse flow elution" should never be used in the ion exchange separation of complex mixtures. Under such conditions early desorbing substances would have to migrate through all other bound species, possibly displacing them, and lead to lost resolution.

Gradient generation

Accurate and reproducible pH and ionic strength gradients are best formed using purpose designed equipment. The choice of gradient generating system will depend upon the type of ion exchange media and the required complexity of the gradient.

Gradient Mixer

The Pharmacia Gradient Mixer GM-1 can be used to make linear ionic strength or pH gradients of up to 500 ml in volume (Fig. 41). The mixing chamber should contain the starting buffer and the other chamber the limiting buffer.

Although the Gradient Mixer GM-1 will not produce linear pH gradients it can be used to form reproducible continuous pH gradients from two solutions of different pH and similar ionic strength.

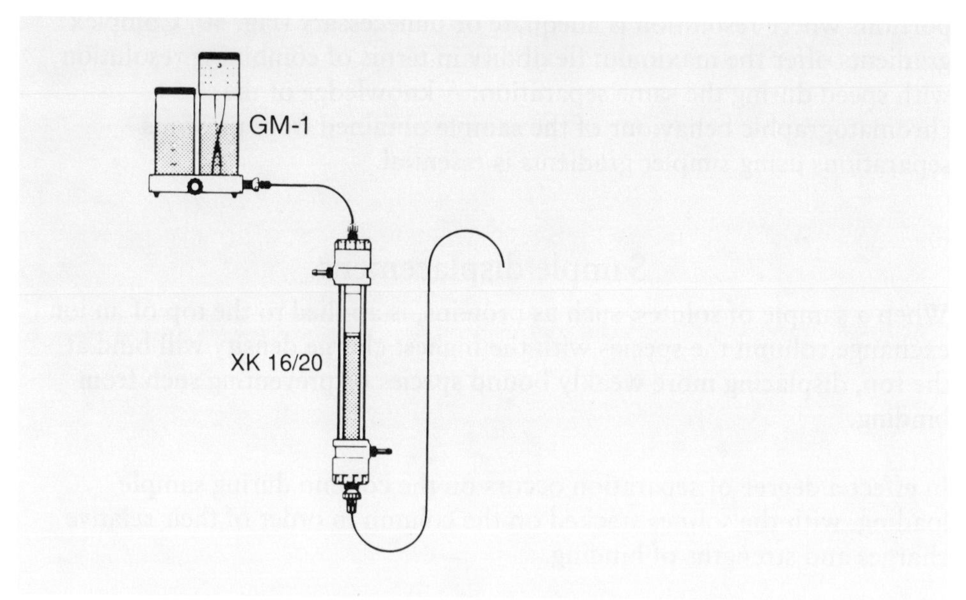

Fig. 41. Gradient elution system using the Gradient Mixer GM-1.

An example of a decreasing pH gradient produced by the Gradient Mixer GM-1 is shown in Figure 42. The gradient was produced from 0.1 M solutions of Tris (free base), pH 10.5 and Tris-HCl, pH 7.5.

Usually changes in pH also produce small changes in ionic strength. These can be estimated by monitoring conductivity.

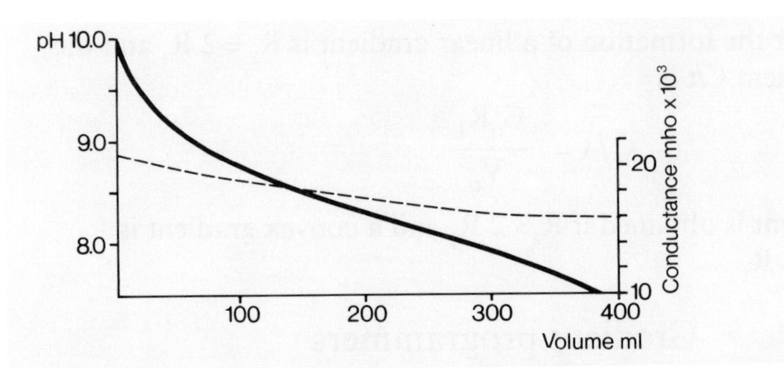

Fig. 42. Gradient from pH 10.5 to 7.5 in 400 ml produced using the Gradient Mixer GM-1. pH —, conductance – – –. (Work from Pharmacia, Uppsala, Sweden.).

Three-channel Peristaltic Pumps

Linear, convex and concave gradients can also be made using the Pharmacia Peristaltic Pump P-3. All that is required is the pump, two vessels and a stirrer (Fig. 43)

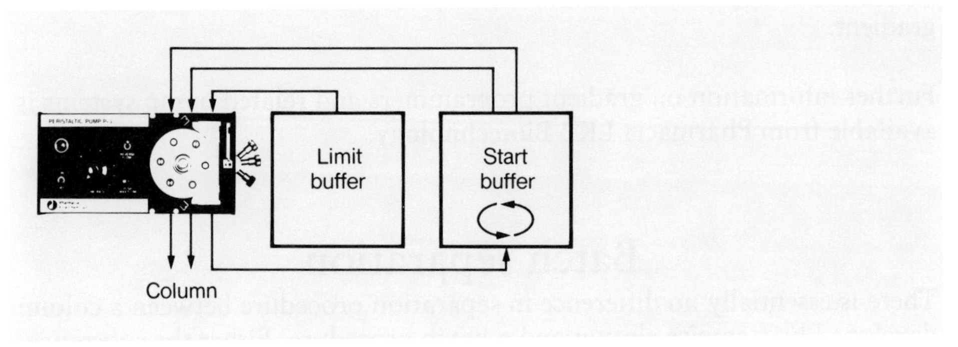

Fig. 43. Set-up for gradient formation with Peristaltic Pump P-3.

The form and volume of the concentration gradient produced using the equipment shown in Figure 43 is completely specified by the flow rates R_1 (from the limit buffer to the mixing chamber) and R_2 (from the mixing chamber to the column), the concentration C_0 of the limit buffer and the initial volume V_0 in the mixing chamber (30).

Linear gradients are particularly easy to generate (31). Each of the three channels is fitted with the same size pump tubing. Two channels are used to pump the gradient out of the mixing chamber and the third channel is used to pump limit buffer into the mixing chamber.

The condition for the formation of a linear gradient is $R_2 = 2\ R_1$ and the slope of the gradient C/t is

$$C/t = \frac{C_0 R_1}{V_0}$$

A concave gradient is obtained if $R_2 > 2\ R_1$ and a convex gradient is obtained if $R_2 < 2\ R_1$.

Gradient programmers

Maximum flexibility in terms of gradient production is achieved by using a gradient programmer which controls two separate pumps for start and limit buffers or a single pump in combination with a switch valve.

Using the gradient programmer the proportions of the start and limit buffers which constitute the eluent being supplied to the column are programmed for specific times or volumes during the separation. The relative amounts of start and limit buffer then increase or decrease in a linear fashion between two such "breakpoints" to produce the gradient. The more breakpoints which have been programmed the more complex the gradient.

Further information on gradient programmers and related pump systems is available from Pharmacia LKB Biotechnology.

Batch separation

There is essentially no difference in separation procedure between a column developed by stepwise elution and a batch procedure. Either the substance of interest or contaminants may be attached to the ion exchanger.

Although batch procedures are less efficient than column techniques they may offer advantages in particular cases. Batch separation is a very rapid technique and no technical difficulties are caused by the swelling or shrinkage of Sephadex ion exchangers. The shrinkage may even be an advantage in some applications.

Batch separation is carried out by stirring the ion exchanger previously equilibrated in the appropriate buffer with the solution to be treated until the mixture has reached equilibrium. This usually takes about one hour. The slurry is then filtered and washed with the buffer solution. In cases of incomplete adsorption this procedure should be repeated on the filtrate

with a new batch of ion exchanger. The absorbed substance can be desorbed fractionally from the ion exchanger by re-suspending the slurry in buffer solutions of higher ionic strength or modified pH or by packing the slurry in a column and eluting as described in the previous section.
In batch chromatography the protein sample is bound uniformly throughout the gel slurry and subsequent chromatographic bed. Under these conditions stepwise elution is recommended since gradient elution will give broad bands and poor resolution.

Batch chromatography is very useful for concentrating dilute solutions and separating the substances of interest from gross contaminants during the initial stages of a purification scheme.

Note: Fines will be generated if the ion exchangers are stirred too vigorously. This will increase the time required for filtration.

Regeneration and storage

Sephadex ion exchangers

Wash with salt solution until an ionic strength of about 2 M has been reached. This should remove any substances bound by ionic forces. The salt should contain the counter-ion to the ion exchanger to facilitate equilibration.

Contaminants such as lipids, proteins etc. can be removed by washing with 0.1 M NaOH followed by distilled water, buffer or salt solution until free from alkali. Lipids may also be removed by washing with alcohol solutions or non-ionic detergents.

DEAE Sephacel

Regeneration of DEAE Sephacel can be carried out in the column. Normally, high salt concentration solutions can be used to remove substances bound by ionic forces. More strongly bound substances can be removed by washing with 0.1 M NaOH or cationic detergents.

Sepharose Based ion exchangers

Regeneration of Sepharose based ion exchangers is particularly easy since this can be done in the column without the need for repacking. Washing the column with a high ionic strength salt solution, e.g. 1 M NaCl, or changing the pH is normally sufficient to remove all reversibly bound material from the column. Regeneration for re-use is accomplished by re-equilibrating the ion exchanger with the desired buffer solution.

When necessary, lipids, precipitated proteins etc. can be washed from the column with one bed volume of 0.5 -2.0 M NaOH followed immediately by rinsing.

MonoBeads columns

Reversibly bound substances which have not been eluted during the separation can be washed from the column using one column volume of high ionic strength solution, e.g. 2 M NaCl. The column is then ready for equilibration with the desired starting buffer for the next separation.

Due to the small particle size of MonoBeads, Mono S and Mono Q are more sensitive to particulate matter such as precipitated proteins from the sample or buffer solutions than the larger bead size matrices. Preventative measures to ensure cleanliness of the sample and buffers are essential to ensure long column life. Such procedures are described in earlier. Should precipitated material be present, as indicated by a decrease in performance or an increase in back pressure, the columns may be cleaned using the detailed instructions included with the column.

Storage

As well as endangering the sample, bacterial and microbial growth can seriously interfere with the chromatographic properties of ion exchange columns and may obstruct the flow through the bed. During storage an antimicrobial agent should be added to the ion exchanger. The antimicrobial agent should be chosen so that it is not bound to the ion exchanger.

Antimicrobial agents for anion exchangers:
Phenyl mercuric salts, 0.001%, effective in weakly alkaline solutions.
Hibitane, (Chlorohexidine) 0.002%.

Antimicrobial agents for cation exchangers:
Merthiolate (Thimerosal, ethyl mercuric thiosalicylate) 0.005%, mostly effective in weakly acidic solution.

Antimicrobial agents for anion and cation exchangers:
Chloretone (trichlorobutanol), 0.05%, effective only in weakly acidic solutions.

Antimicrobial agents for BioProcess Media:
Sodium hydroxide up to 1.0 M will significantly lower the bacterial count (>100 times) and solubilize dead cells. This method will not leave any toxic materials on the column, a significant factor in pharmaceutical production. Specific protocols are available on request.

Note: For DEAE Sephacel, Sepharose based ion exchangers and MonoBeads based ion exchangers, the antimicrobial agent of choice is 20% ethanol.

Scale-up

Frequently ion exchange separations are carried out initially on a small scale to optimize conditions before commitment of the sample to full scale separations. It is thus important to choose an ion exchanger which will allow simple and convenient scale up so that methods established on a small column can be applied more or less directly to the larger column.

Scaling-up in ion exchange chromatography can be approached in two different ways:

1. Using the same ion exchanger in a larger diameter column

2. Using an ion exchanger with the same charged group but substituted on a high throughput matrix.

The correct approach to scale-up is to use the same medium throughout. In this case scale-up of an optimized experiment is achieved by using simple scale factors to account for the increased volumes (39).

The scale factor for the volumetric flow rate is the ratio between the cross-sectional areas for the two columns, i.e. the same linear flow rate is maintained.

The scale factor for the gradient volume is the ratio between the column volumes, i.e. maintain the gradient volume : bed volume ratio.

The scale factor for the sample loading is the ratio between the column volumes, i.e. maintain the sample loading : bed volume ratio.

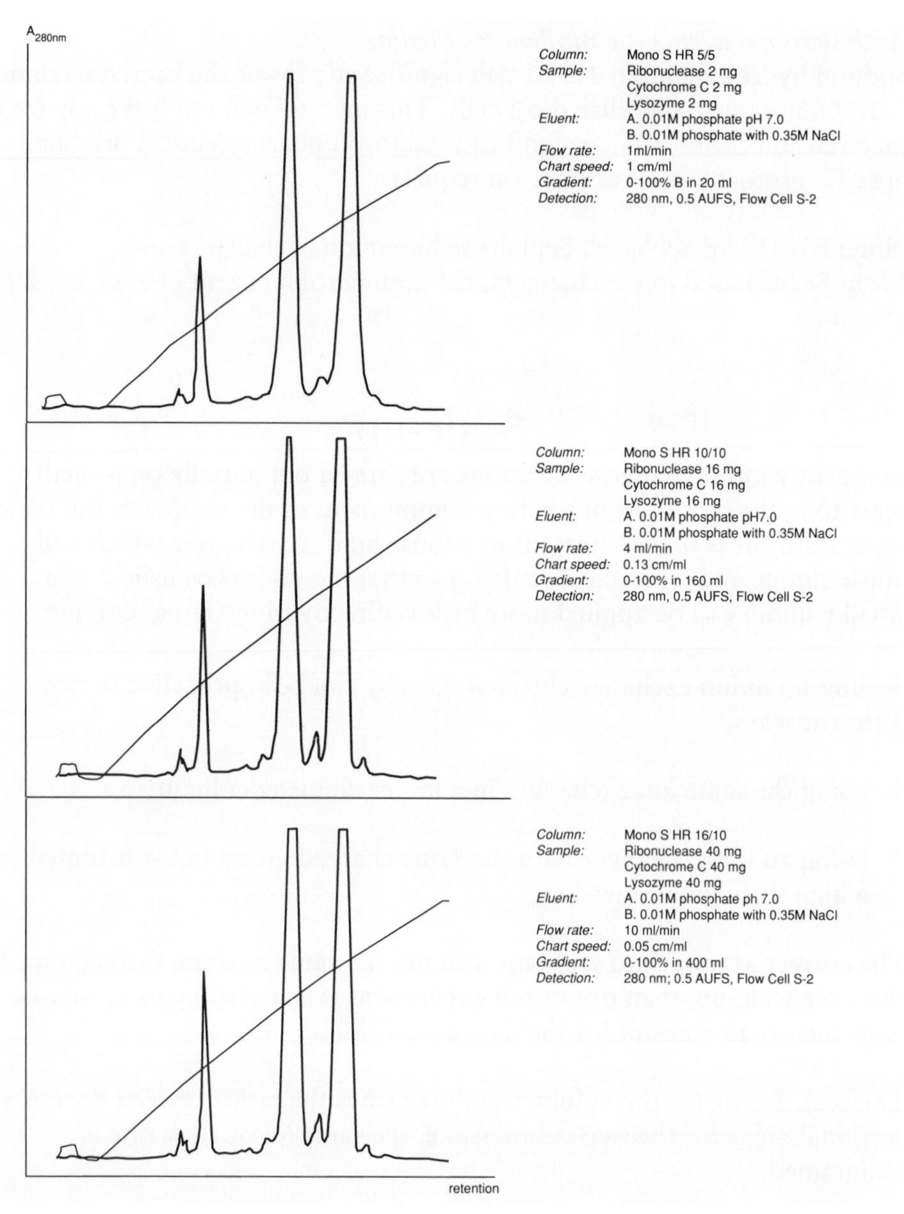

Fig. 44. Separation of model proteins on Mono S at three different scales. (Work from Pharmacia, Uppsala, Sweden.).

This type of scale-up is illustrated in Figure 44 which shows the scale-up of a separation of model proteins on Mono S. The appropriate scaling factors, which also apply to Mono Q columns are given in Table 15.

Table 15. Factors for scaling up from Mono S HR 5/5 (1 ml) to Mono S HR 10/10 (8 ml) to Mono S HR 16/10 (20 ml)

Column	Gradient Volume	Flow rate	Sample Loading
Mono S HR5/5	x1	x1	x1
Mono S HR10/10	x8	x4 (up to 6 ml/min)	x8
Mono S HR16/10	x20	x10 (up to10 ml/min)	x20

Similar factors can be calculated for other media for different size columns. These factors only apply when scale-up is done on the same ion exchange medium.

The second scale-up case is when the base matrix is changed. An example of this would be the scale-up of an analytical separation on a 10 µm matrix (MonoBeads) to a high through-put matrix such as Sepharose Fast Flow. In this situation it is important that the two media have the same charged substituents and consequently similar selectivities. Under these conditions scale factors similar to those above can be used. They must however, be corrected for the differences in the base matrices and the following formulae have been used in the scale-up from Mono Q and Mono S columns (A) to larger columns (B) packed with Q and S Sepharose Fast Flow.

$$\text{Volumetric flow rate B} = \text{Volumetric flow rate A} \times \frac{\text{column area B}}{\text{column area A}} \times \frac{1}{Y}$$

$$\text{Gradient volume B} = \text{Gradient volume A} \times \frac{\text{column area B}}{\text{column area A}} \times Z$$

Y and Z are empirically found conversion factors. Y lies between 5 and 10; Z lies between 2 and 3.

An example of this type of scale-up is shown in Figure 45. In this example the scale factor corrections were Y = 5 and Z = 2.

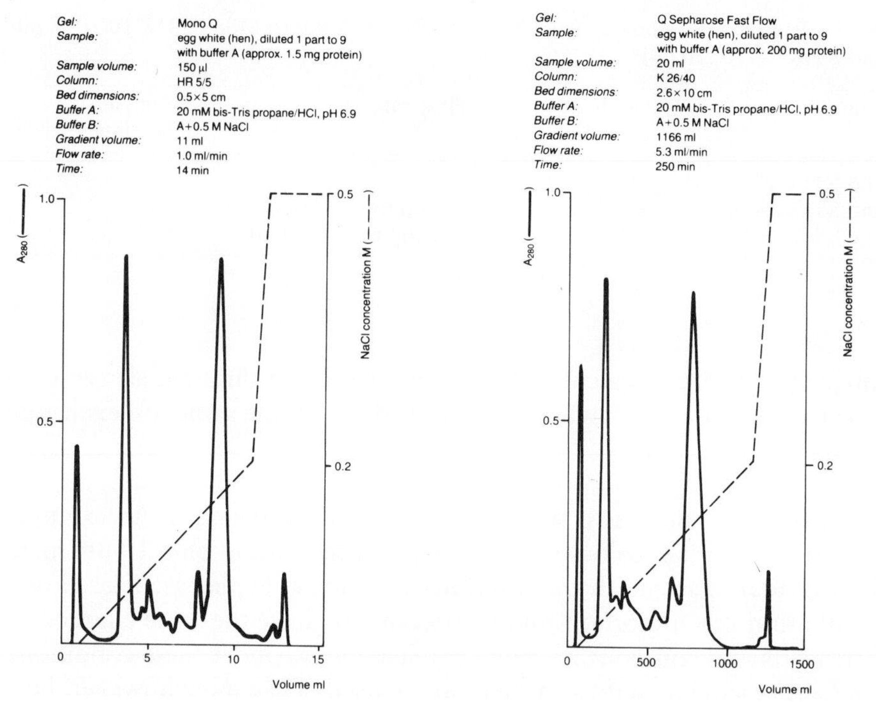

Fig. 45. Scale-up from Mono Q to Q Sepharose Fast Flow. (Work from Pharmacia, Uppsala, Sweden.).

Determination of the available and dynamic capacities.

The available capacity of an ion exchanger can be determined by a batch test-tube method similar to that used for the determination of suitable buffer pH and binding and elution ionic strengths (see page 53 and Fig. 25 d). In this case a series of solutions with different concentrations of the protein are added to a known quantity of ion exchanger, equilibrated at a suitable binding pH and ionic strength. Assaying the supernatants after mixing will show the maximum protein concentration which can be bound per ml of ion exchanger.

For a more realistic and useful measurement of the available capacity of an ion exchanger, a dynamic method is recommended. The type of equipment necessary for this determination is shown in Figure 46. FPLC System can also be used for this determination.

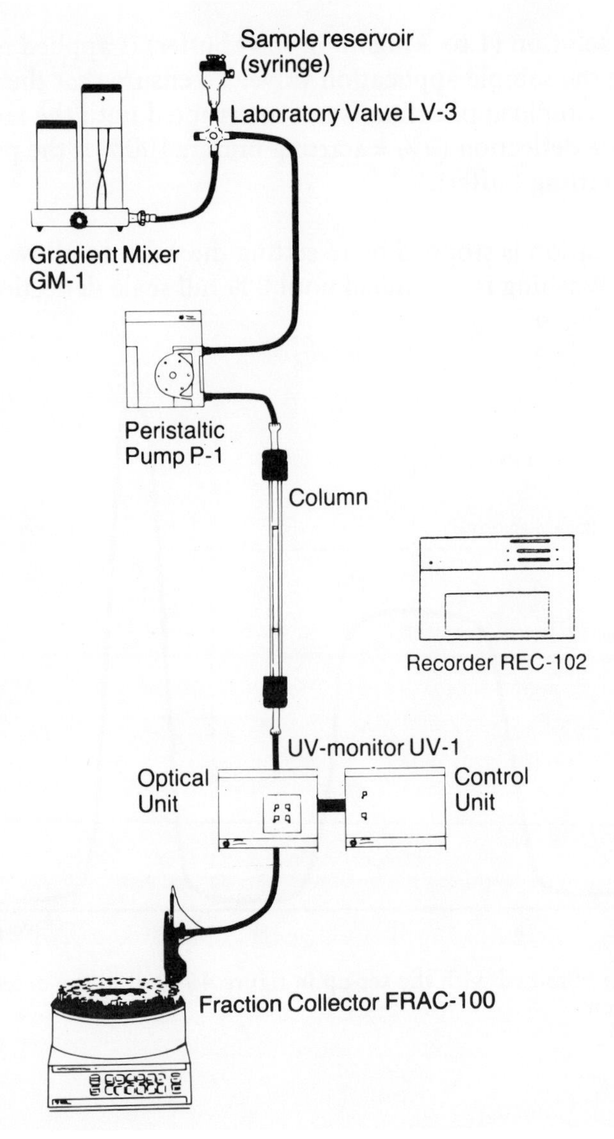

Fig. 46. Experimental set up for the determination of the dynamic capacity of an ion exchanger.

A defined amount of gel is introduced into the column (Normally a quantity of gel sufficient to give a bed volume of approximately 1 ml is sufficient). The gel is packed and equilibrated until the eluate is of the same pH as that of the starting buffer. The exact volume of gel is calculated by means of the known column diameter and by measuring the bed height. In the case of a prepacked column the amount of gel is already predetermined.

The protein solution (1 to 5 mg/ml in start buffer) is applied to the column by switching the sample application valve. To ensure that the column is fully loaded, sample application is not interrupted until the recorder shows 50% full scale deflection (0% = starting buffer; 100% = the protein solution in starting buffer).

Sample application is stopped by re-setting the valve to allow passage of start buffer. Washing is continued until 0% full scale deflection (FSD) is approached (Fig. 47).

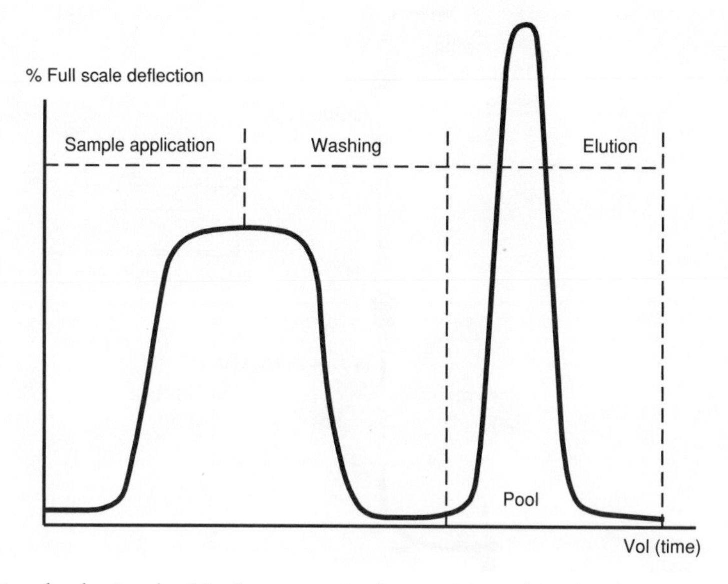

Fig. 47. Graph obtained with the set-up in figure 46 used in the determination of dynamic capacity.

After the wash phase, adsorbed protein is eluted with a stepwise change in ionic strength (e.g. 2 M NaCl) or pH. Fractions are collected as long as the UV-absorption is above 2% FSD. These fractions are pooled and the UV-absorption of the pool is measured.

Calculation

The maximum amount of protein that can be bound to the column (A) at the chosen flow rate is:

$$A = C \times V$$

C = The protein concentration in the pooled fractions (mg/ml).
V = volume of pooled fractions..

$$C = A_{280} / E$$

A_{280} = absorbance of solution at 280 nm in 1 cm cell.
E = absorbance of standard solution (1 mg/ml) at 280 nm in 1 cm cell.

The protein capacity is calculated as:

A/gel volume

This calculation assumes that the recovery of bound protein from the column is 100%. This can be checked by comparison with the quantity of protein applied to the column.

10. Applications

Ion exchange has proved to be one of the major methods of fractionation of labile biological substances. From the introduction of the technique in the 1960s´ to the development of modern high performance media, ion exchange chromatography has played a major role in the separation and purification of biomolecules and contributed significantly to our understanding of biological processes. The examples given in the following section have been drawn from the published literature as well as from work in our own laboratories.

For detailed information on specific subjects the reader is referred to the original work.

The design of a biochemical separation

Ion exchange chromatography, in common with other separation techniques in the life sciences, is rarely sufficient as the sole purification stage in the separation or analysis of complex biological samples. Ion exchange is frequently combined with other techniques which separate according to other parameters such as size (gel filtration), hydrophobicity (hyrophobic interaction chromatography or RPC) or biological activity (affinity chromatography).

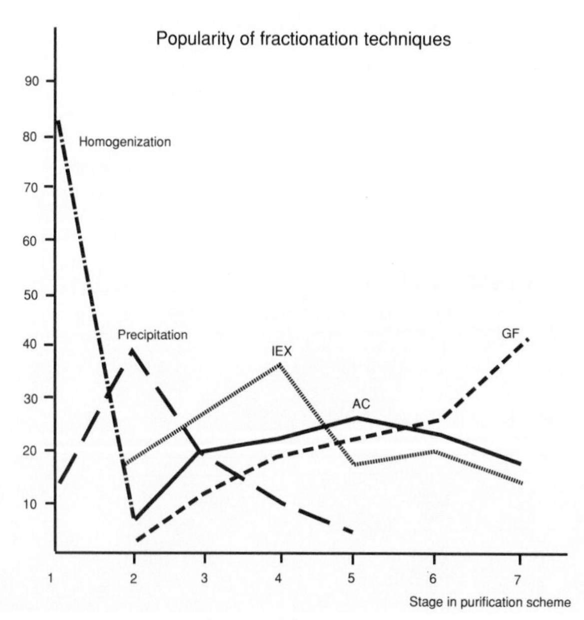

Fig. 48. Frequency of use of fractionation techniques (1). Reproduced by kind permission of the authors and publisher.

Not only is the choice of techniques important. The order in which they are employed will also play a role in determining the speed, the convenience and the overall yield for the purification.

Sample loading, sample dilution and impurity contamination are usually maximal at the beginning of a separation scheme. At this stage the high capacity, high selectivity and concentrating effect of ion exchange makes the technique ideal.

This suitability is reflected in Figure 48 which shows the frequency of use of different fractionation techniques in published protein purification schemes (1).

The use of multi-dimensional chromatography with ion exchange as a first step is well illustrated by the separation of monoclonal IgG_{2b} from cell culture medium (Fig. 49). An initial purification and concentration of the antibody from 500 ml cell culture medium by cation exchange

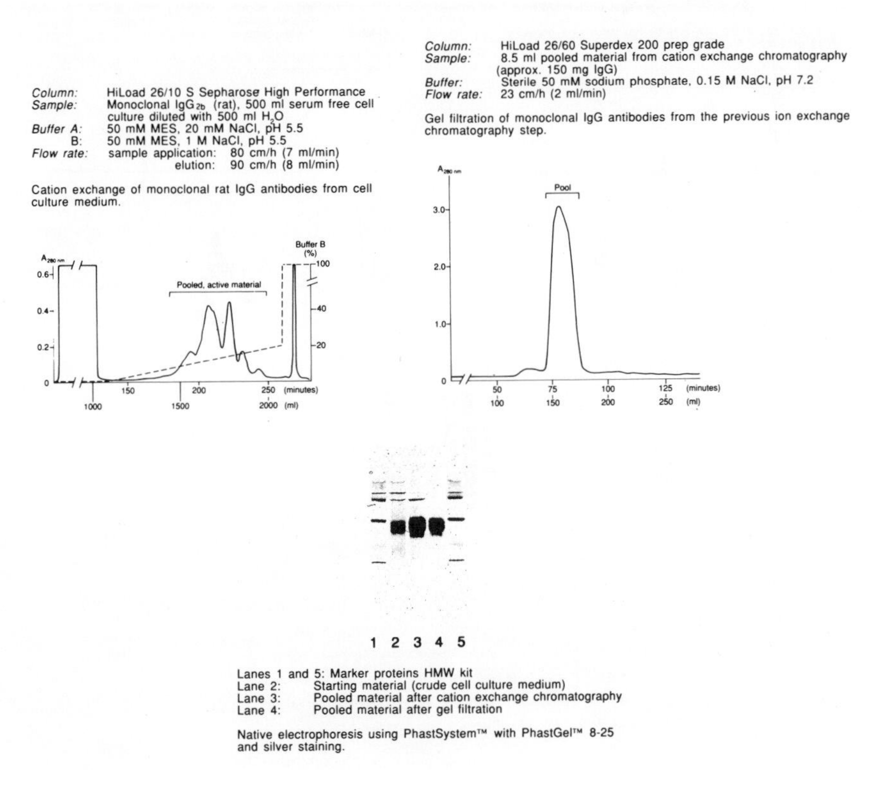

Fig. 49. Purification of rat monoclonal IgG_{2b} from cell culture supernatant. (Work from Pharmacia, Uppsala, Sweden.).

chromatography on S Sepharose High Performance was followed by a second fractionation by gel filtration using Superdex 200 prep grade.

The sample composition with regards to ionic strength and pH should be taken into consideration when designing the separation scheme. In ion exchange chromatography solutes bind to the gel at low ionic strength and are eluted from the column at a higher ionic strength. The converse situation occurs in hydrophobic interaction chromatography. Thus if these two techniques are to be used in a separation scheme it is logical to have them adjacent to each other. This principle is illustrated in Figure 50 which shows the purification of human α2-macroglobulin from Cohn Fraction III.

After initial purification by affinity chromatography on Blue Sepharose CL-6B to remove albumin, the sample was applied to a Q Sepharose High

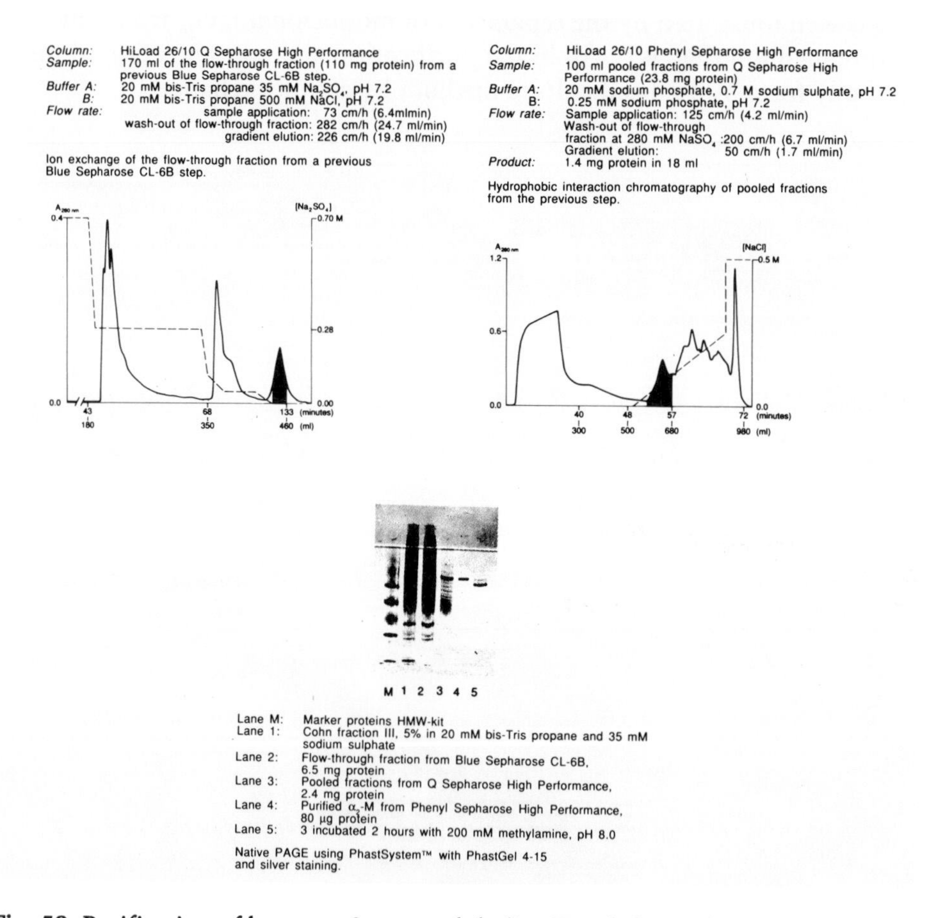

Fig. 50. Purification of human α2-macroglobulin. (Work from Pharmacia, Uppsala, Sweden.).

Performance column and eluted with an increasing salt concentration gradient. Relevant fractions were then pooled and α2-macroglobulin was purified to homogeneity by hydrophobic interaction chromatography on a Phenyl Sepharose High Performance column.

Towards the end of a separation scheme the complexity and the volume of sample to be handled is smaller, but in most cases the need for higher resolution is increased. Ion exchange chromatography, particularly with Sepharose High Performance or MonoBeads media can also be used at this stage (Fig. 51).

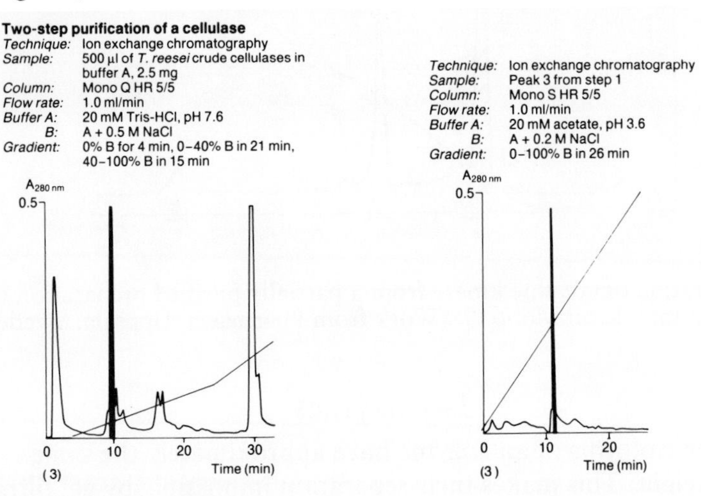

Fig. 51. Use of ion exchange in the final purification of cellulase. (Work from Pharmacia, Uppsala, Sweden.).

Application examples

Ion exchange chromatography has been used successfully to separate all classes of charged biological molecules. The following are some representative examples.

Enzymes

In the purification of biologically active proteins such as enzymes the recovery of biological activity is usually as important as the recovery of protein mass or degree of homogeneity. Ion exchange chromatography has played a role in the purification of thousands of enzymes, and using modern matrices with optimized separation conditions gives extremely high recoveries. This is exemplified by the separation of enzymes from chicken breast muscle on Mono Q (Fig. 52). The recovery of creatine kinase in this separation was 89%.

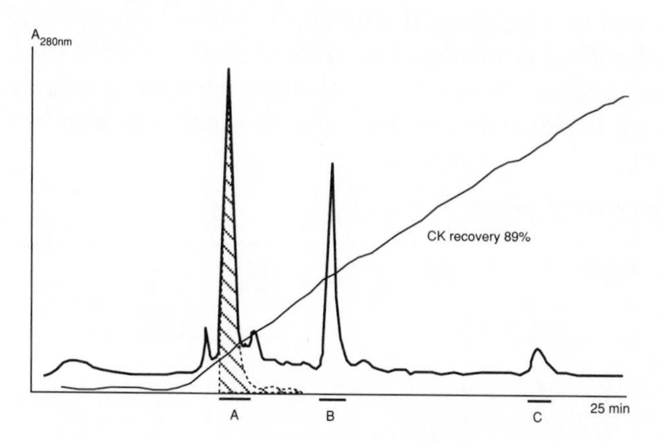

Fig. 52. Separation of creatine kinase from a partially purified preparation of chicken breast muscle on Mono Q. (Work from Pharmacia, Uppsala, Sweden.).

Isoenzymes

Normally the isoforms of an enzyme have approximately the same molecular weight. This makes their separation impossible by gel filtration. However, the small differences in charge properties resulting from altered amino acid composition enable the separation of isoenzymes using ion exchange chromatography.

N-Acetyl β–D-glucosiminidases have been widely investigated in the diagnosis of haematological malignancies. In the case of common acute lymphoblastic leukaemia, an isoenzyme, referred to as "Intermediate 1 Form" has been reported (32). Using high resolution ion exchange chromatography (Fig. 53) this previously "single" peak has been resolved into a number of component isoenzymes which had previously only been detectable using isoelectric focusing.

Immunoglobulins

Ion exchange is frequently used for the purification of immunoglobulins. Figure 49 shows the purification of rat monoclonal IgG_{2b} from cell culture supernatatant. As illustrated in Figure 54 the technique can also be applied to the purification of monoclonal immunoglobulin from ascites fluid.

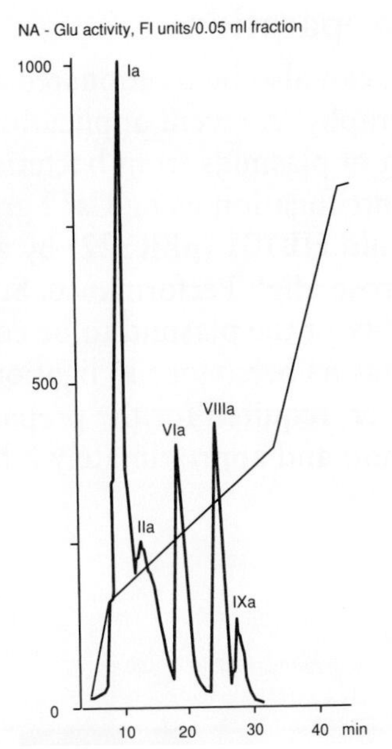

Fig. 53. Separation of Leukaemic cell N- Acetyl b-D-glucosaminidase isoenzymes by anion exchange chromatography on Mono Q. NA-Glu activities associated with disinct peaks (Ia-IXa) are indicated in relation to the NaCl gradient (32). Reproduced by kind permission of the authors and publisher.

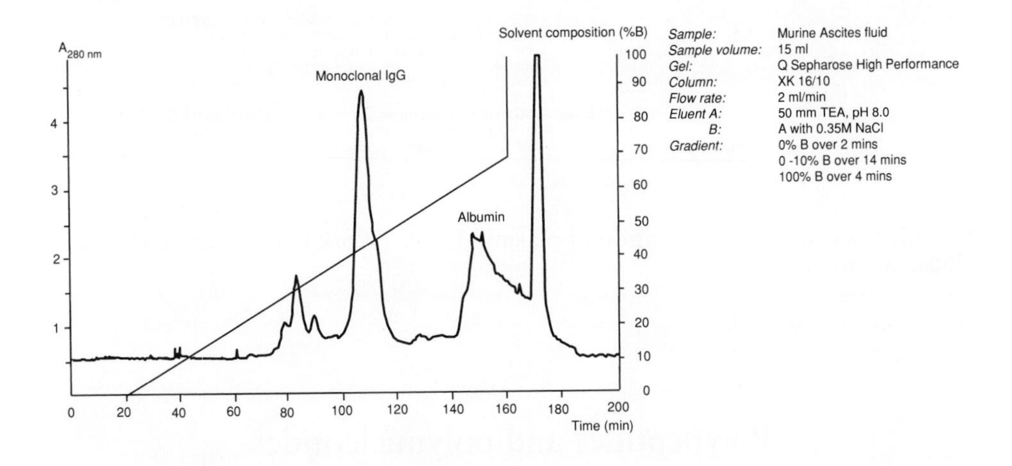

Fig. 54. Ion exchange purification of mouse monoclonal IgG_1 from ascites fluid. Reproduced by kind permission of Dr. LeRoy Baker, Eli Research Laboratories, Eli Lilly and Company, Indianapolis, USA.

Nucleic acid separation

Nucleic acids, being charged molecules, can also be fractionated and purified using ion exchange chromatography. A recent application of the technique in this area is the purification of plasmids from bacterial cultures. This process is traditionally done by centrifugation using CsCl gradients. Figure 55 shows the separation of plasmid HB101 (pBR322) by anion exchange chromatography on Q Sepharose High Performance. Subsequent analysis showed the electrophoretic purity of the plasmid to be equivalent to that obtained by centrifugation, as was its behaviour in ligation and transformation assays. The time, however, required for the preparation was 1 hour using the chromatographic method and approximately 8 hours using centrifugation.

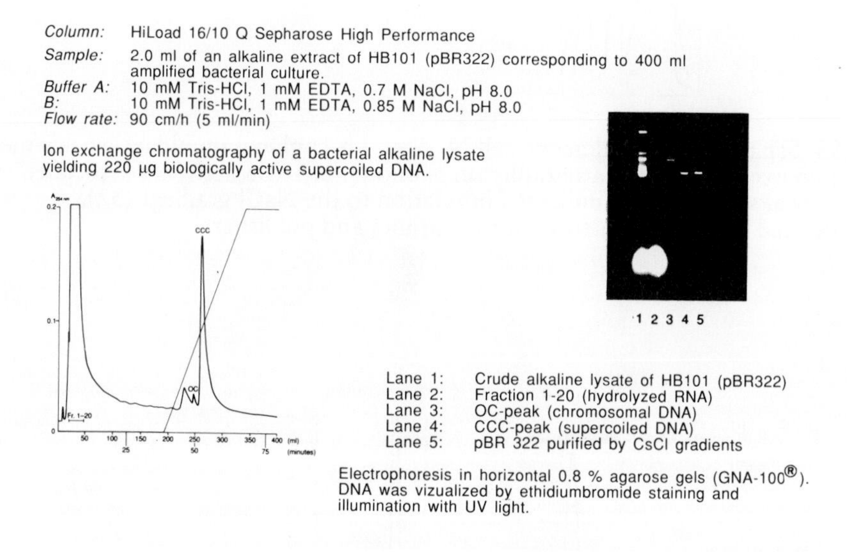

Fig. 55. Ion exchange purification of plasmid DNA. (Work from Pharmacia, Uppsala, Sweden.).

Polypeptides and polynucleotides

Ion exchange chromatography is not limited in its application to macromolecules such as proteins and nucleic acids. The technique can be used in the separation of peptides as illustrated by the separation of cyanogen bromide fragments of collagen (Fig. 56).

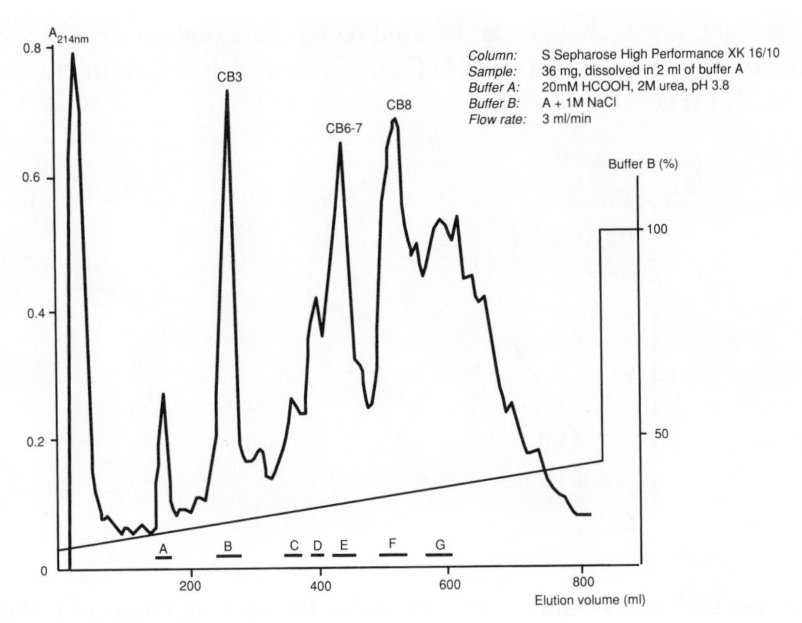

Fig. 56. Separation of CNBr-peptides from a-1 chains of collagen type1. (Work from Pharmacia, Uppsala, Sweden.).

In peptide mapping applications ion exchange chromatography can be used advantageously as a complement to reverse phase chromatography since both offer high resolution but separate according to different parameters (33).

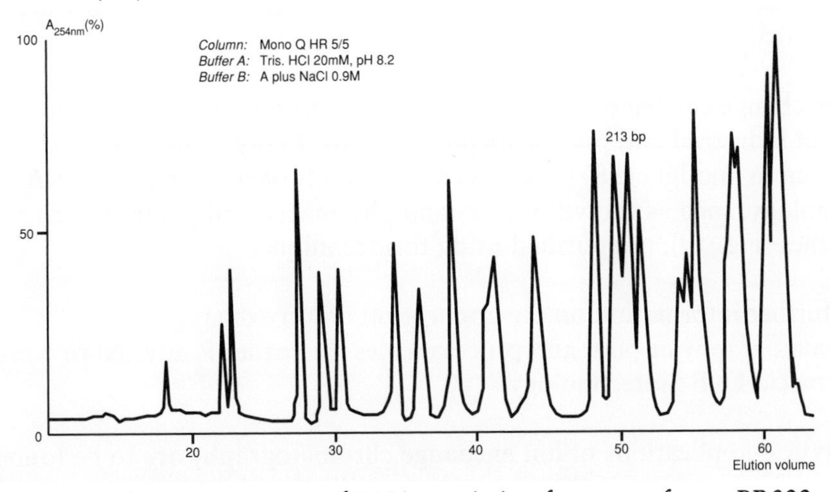

Fig. 57. Ion exchange separation of DNA restriction fragments from pBR322 cleaved by HaeIII (34). Reproduced by kind permission of the authors and publisher.

Analogously, ion exchange can be used to separate oligonucleotides such as restriction fragments of DNA (34) (Fig. 57) and even individual nucleotides (35, 36, 37) (Fig. 58).

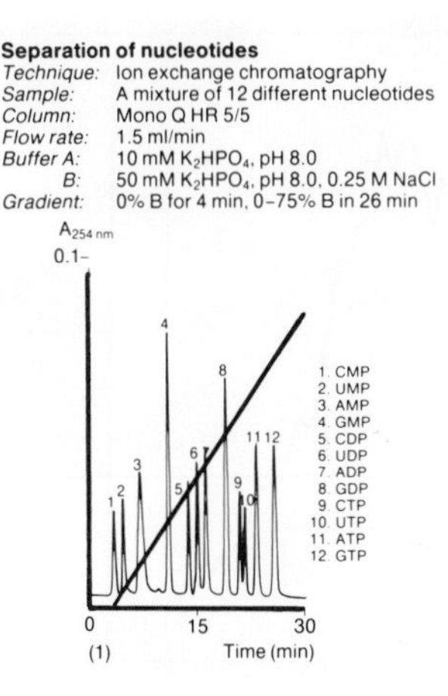

Fig. 58. Ion exchange separation of nucleotides. (Work from Pharmacia, Uppsala, Sweden.).

Areas of application

In the preceding chapters the examples which have been used to illustrate the principles and practice of ion exchange chromatography have mostly been based on analytical and preparative applications from the research laboratory.

Ion exchange chromatography also has many important applications in the field of industrial and pilot scale preparations. Many blood products such as albumin and IgG (38) as well as the products of recombinant DNA technology, such as growth factors and pharmaceutically important enzymes (Fig. 59), are purified using this technique.

For further information on the application of ion exchange chromatography at pilot and process scales the reader is advised to contact Pharmacia LKB Biotechnology.

Analytical applications of ion exchange chromatography are to be found in diverse areas such as quality control of purified products or process monitoring in biotechnology. Figure 60 shows the use of cation exchange in monitoring a fermentation process for the production of β-galactosidase.

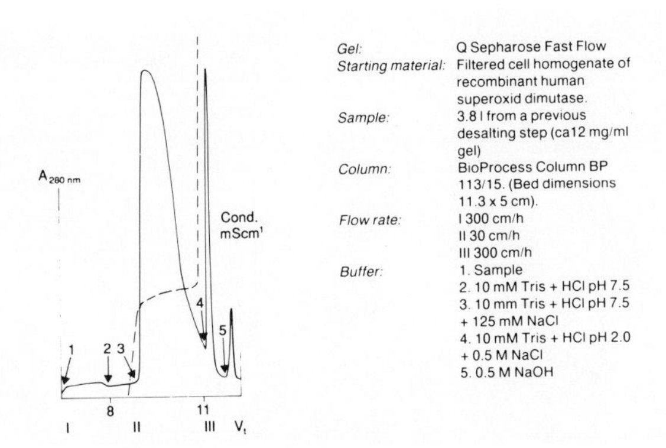

Fig. 59. Process scale purification of recombinant superoxide dismutase by ion exchange chromatography on Q Sepharose Fast Flow. (Work from Pharmacia, Uppsala, Sweden.).

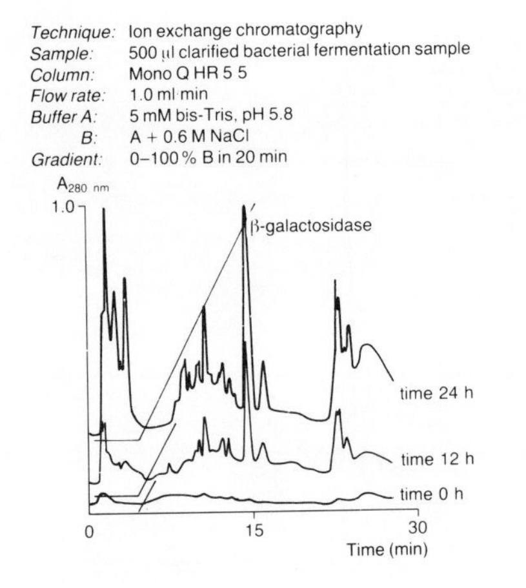

Fig. 60. Monitoring the production of β-galactosidase (40).

Other areas of application include food research where FPLC ion exchange can be used in the study of wheat varietals (Fig. 61) and in clinical research where ion exchange chromatography has been used in studies such as the relationship between post-partum depression and β-endorphin secretion (Fig. 62) and the correlation of proteinuria with different renal conditions (Fig. 63).

A chromatogram of the urine from patients exhibiting tubular proteinuria, due to acute pyelonephritis, severe burns or renal transplants, shows distinct peaks corresponding to β2-microglobulin, retinol binding protein and α1-acid glycoprotein. The disappearance of these peaks could be correlated with the reversal of their causal lesion (43).

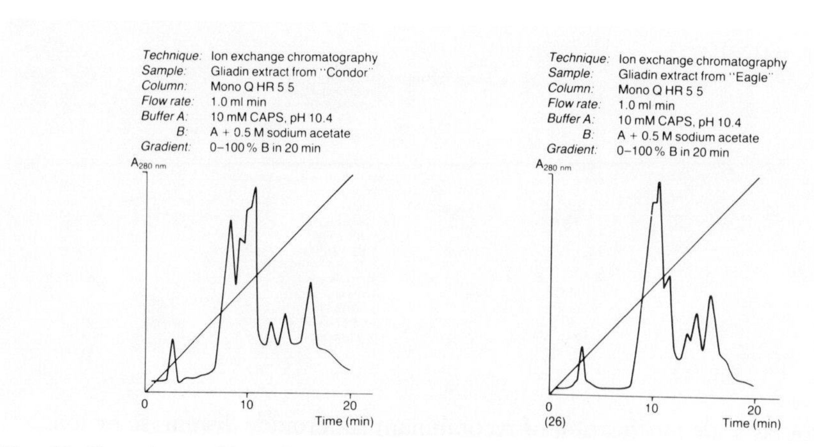

Fig. 61. Protein profiles of wheat varietal gliadins (41).

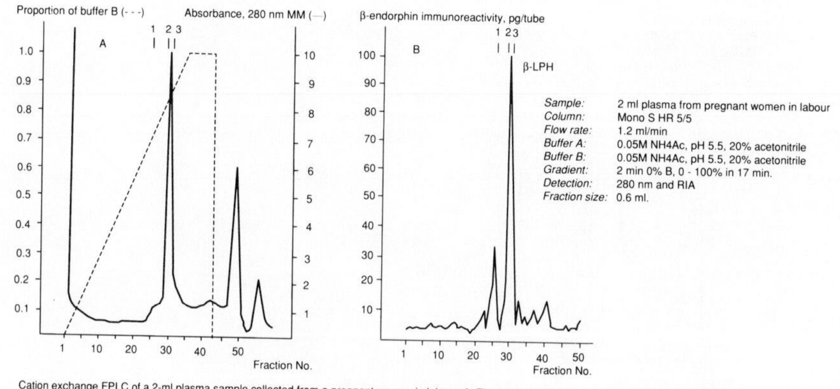

Cation exchange FPLC of a 2-ml plasma sample collected from a pregnant woman in labour. A. The elution pattern (—) of UV-absorbing material,and the concentration of buffer B (- - -) . B. Elution of β-endorphin immunoreactivity : the position of elution of reference β-endorphin in (1). [^{125}I] β-endorphin (2) and β-lipotropin are shown by the vertical lines.

Fig. 62. Cation exchange chromatography of plasma b-endorphin(42).

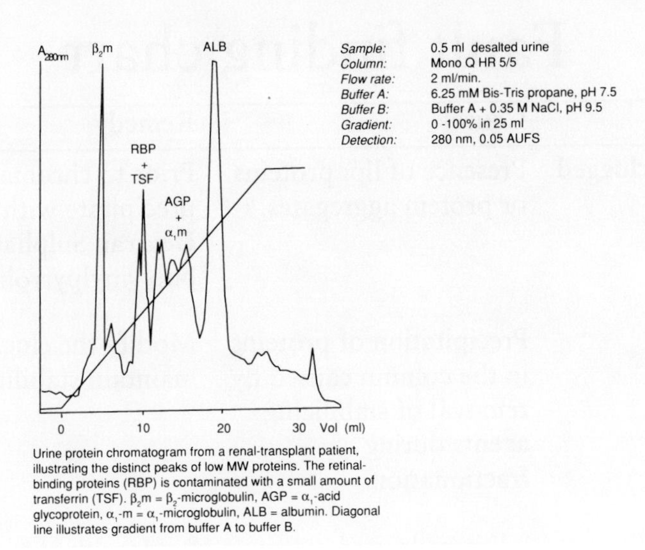

Urine protein chromatogram from a renal-transplant patient, illustrating the distinct peaks of low MW proteins. The retinal-binding proteins (RBP) is contaminated with a small amount of transferrin (TSF). β_2m = β_2-microglobulin, AGP = α_1-acid glycoprotein, α_1-m = α_1-microglobulin, ALB = albumin. Diagonal line illustrates gradient from buffer A to buffer B.

Fig. 63. Anion exchange of urine in renal proteinuria (43).

Fault finding chart

Problem	Cause	Remedy
Column is clogged	Presence of lipoproteins or protein aggregates.	Prior to chromatography, precipitate with 10% Dextran Sulphate or 3% polyvinylpyrrolidone.
	Precipitation of proteins in the column caused by removal of stabilizing agents during fractionation.	Modify the eluent to maintain stability.
	Filter is clogged.	Replace the filter. Always filter samples and buffer before use.
	Microbial growth has occurred in the column.	Microbial growth rarely occurs in columns during use, but steps should always be taken to prevent infection of packed columns, buffers and gel suspensions. Store gel in the presence of 20% ethanol or an antimicrobial agent.
No flow through the column	Outlet closed.	Open outlet.
	No flow from pump	With peristaltic pumps check the condition of the tubings. Check for leaks at all connections.
	Clogged end-piece or adaptor or tubing.	Remove and clean, if possible.
Reduced or poor flow through the column	Bed surface blocked by precipitated proteins.	Clean using recommended methods

Problem	Cause	Remedy
Reduced or poor flow through the column	Bed compressed.	Repacking the column may be necessary.*
	Microbial growth.	Microbial growth rarely occurs in columns during use, but steps should always be taken to prevent infection of packed columns, buffers and gel suspensions. Store gel in the presence of 20% ethanol or an antimicrobial agent.
	Fines	Do not use a magnetic stirrer; it can break the beads.
Back pressure increases during a run or during successive runs.	Turbid sample has been applied to the column.	Improve sample solubility by the addition of monoethylene glycol, detergents or organic solvents.
	Clogged column filter.	Prefilter buffers and samples. Change filter.
	Precipitation of protein in the column filter and/ or at the top of the gel bed.	Clean the column and exchange or clean the filter.
		Change pH and/or add urea. Develop a procedure with detergents.
		Additives which were used for initial sample solubilization should be included in the solutions used for chromatography.

* Does not apply for prepacked columns.

Problem	Cause	Remedy
Back pressure increases during a run or during successive runs.	Precipitation of lipoproteins at increased ionic strength	Lipoproteins may be precipitated prior to chromatography by the addition of 10% dextran sulphate and 1 M calcium chloride to final concentrations of 0.2% and 0.5 M respectively.
The protein does not elute in the salt gradient.	Incorrect buffer pH.	Use a buffer pH closer to the pI of the protein.
	Ionic strength too low.	Use a more concentrated limit buffer.
The protein does not elute.	Solutions have wrong pH.	Calibrate your pH meter, prepare new solutions and try again.
Protein elutes in the wash phase.	Ionic strength of start buffer is too high.	Decrease ionic strength of start buffer.
	The ionic strength of the sample is too high or the pH is wrong.	Buffer exchange on sample.
	The column is not properly equilibrated.	Repeat or prolong the equilibration step.
	Ionic detergents or other additives are adsorbed to the column.	Clean the column.
The resolution obtained is less than expected.	The gradient slope is too steep.	Use a shallower gradient or a plateau in the gradient.
	Microbial growth has occurred in the column.	See above.

Problem	Cause	Remedy
The resolution obtained is less than expected.	Flow rate is too high.	Run the separation at a lower flow rate.
	Proteins or lipids have precipitated on the column.	Clean and regenerate the column.
	Improper filtration of the sample before application to the column.	Regenerate the column, filter the sample and repeat the chromatography step.
	Aggregate formation of proteins in sample and strong binding to gel.	Use urea or zwitterions, betaine up to 10% or taurine up to 4%.
	Column is poorly packed.	Check the packing by running a coloured compound and observing the band. Repack the column if necessary.*
	Too much sample mass has been loaded onto the column.	Decrease the sample load.
	The column is dirty.	Clean and regenerate the column.
	Detector cell volume is too big.	Change the flow cell.
	Large mixing spaces in or after column.	Reduce all post column volumes.
Leading or very rounded peaks observed in the chromatogram	Overloaded column.	Decrease the sample load and repeat the run.

* Does no apply for prepacked columns.

Problem	Cause	Remedy
Leading or very rounded peaks observed in the chromatogram	Column is poorly packed.	Check the packing by running a coloured compound and observing the band. Repack the column if necessary.*
	Column needs regeneration.	Clean and regenerate the column. If this does not help replace with a new one.
Tailing of the peak is observed in the chromatogram. of protein.	Sample too viscous.	Reduce the amount of protein.
	Precipitation of protein in the column filter and/ or at the top of the gel bed.	Remove nucleic acids. Clean the column and exchange or clean the filter.
Previous elution profile can not be reproduced	Incorrect buffer pH and ionic strength	Prepare new solutions.
	The sample has altered during storage.	Prepare fresh sample.
	Proteins or lipids have precipitated on the column.	Clean and regenerate the column.
	Sample has not been filtered properly.	Regenerate the column, filter the sample carefully and repeat this step.
	Incomplete equilibration.	Equlibrate until conductivity is constant.

* Does not apply for prepacked columns.

Problem	Cause	Remedy
Previous elution profile can not be reproduced	Aggregate formation of proteins in sample and strong binding to gel.	Use urea or zwitterions, betaine up to 10% or taurine up to 4%.
Low recovery of activity while normal recovery of protein	Sample substance may not be stable in the elution buffers and is therefore inactivated.	Determine the pH and salt stability of the protein.
	Enzyme separated from co-factor or similar.	Test by pooling fractions and repeating the assay.
	Microbial growth.	Microbial growth rarely occurs in columns during use, but steps should always be taken to prevent infection of packed columns, buffers and gel suspensions. Store gel in the presence of 20% ethanol or an antimicrobial agent.
Protein amount in the eluted fractions is much less than expected	The protein may have been degraded by proteases.	Add protease inhibitors to the buffers to prevent proteolytic digestion.
	Adsorbtion to filter during sample preparation.	Use another type of filter or use detergents.
	Microbial growth has occurred in the column.	Microbial growth rarely occurs in columns during use, but steps should always be taken to prevent infection of packed columns, buffers and gel suspensions. Store gel in the presence of 20% ethanol or an antimicrobial agent.

Problem	Cause	Remedy
Protein amount in the eluted fractions is much less than expected	Non-specific adsorption.	Try adding ethylene glycol (e.g. 10%) to the buffers to prevent any hydrophobic interactions.
	Sample precipitates.	May be caused by removal of salts or sample dilution.
	Hydrophobic proteins.	Chaotropic salts may be used for elution.
More activity is recovered than was applied to the column	Different assay conditions have been used before and after the chromatographic step.	Use the same assay conditions for all the assays in your purification scheme.
	Removal of inhibitors during separation.	Replace if necessary.
Peaks too small	Wrong sensitivity range on detector.	Adjust
	Sample absorbs poorly at the chosen wavelength.	Use a different wavelength.
	Recorder range incorrectly set.	Adjust
	Excessive zone broadening	Check the column packing and re-pack if necessary. Check the recorder settings.
Bubbles in the bed	Column packed or stored at cool temperature and then warmed up.	Small bubbles can often be removed by passing well degassed buffer upwards through the column. Column may need to be re-packed. Take special care if buffers are used after storage in a fridge or cold-

Problem	Cause	Remedy
Bubbles in the bed		room. Do not allow column to warm up due to sunshine or heating system. A water-jacket is a good safeguard. Use degassed buffers.
	Eluent not properly de-gassed.	De-gas the eluent thoroughly.
Cracks in the bed	Large air leak in column.	Check all connections for* leaks. Repack the column.
Distorted bands as sample runs into the bed	Air bubble at the top of the column or in the inlet adaptor.	Re-install the adaptor taking care to avoid air bubbles.
	Particles in eluent or sample.	Filter or centrifuge the sample. Protect eluents from dust.
	Clogged or damaged net in upper adaptor.	Dismantle the adaptor, clean or replace the net. Keep particles out of samples and eluents.
Distorted bands as sample passes down bed	Column poorly packed.	Gel suspension too thick or too thin. Bed packed at a temperature different from run. Bed insufficiently packed (too low packing pressure, too short aquilibration). Column packed at too high pressure.
Negative peaks at solvent front.	Refractive index effects.	Buffer exchange the sample to start buffer.
Strange peaks in chromatogram.	Buffer impurities.	Clean the buffer by running it through precolumn.Use high quality reagents.

* Does not apply for prepacked columns.

Problem	Cause	Remedy
Peaks on blank gradients.	Incomplete elution.	Wash the column according to recommended method
Spikes in chromatogram.	Air bubble trapped in UV cell.	Use degassed solutions.
UV baseline rises with gradient	Salt concentration micelle formation.	Work well below or above the CMC or change the gradient so that the increase in UV absorption does not occur while the samples are eluting.
	Impurities in buffers.	Use high quality reagents.

References

1. The right step at the right time. *Bio/Technology, 4, 954-958 (1986)* Bonnerjera, J., Oh, S., Hoare, M., Dunhill, P.

2. Chromatography of Proteins. I. Cellulose ion exchange adsorbents. *J. Amer. Chem. Soc. 78 (1956) 751 755,* Peterson, E.A., Sober, H.A.

3. Chromatography of proteins on ion-exchange adsorbents. *Meth. Enzymol. 22 (1971) 273—286,* Himmelhoch, S.R.

4. Chromatography: a laboratory handbook of chromatographic and electrophoretic techniques. Heftman, E. (Ed.), Van Noostrand Rheinhold Co., New York (1975).

5. Dynamics of chromatography, Part 1, Principles and theory. Giddings, J.C., Keller, R.A. (Eds.), Marcel Dekker Inc., New York (1965).

6. Chromatography of mixed oligonucleotides on DEAE-Sephadex. *Biochemistry 3 (1964) 626—629,* Rushizky, G.W., Bartos, E.M., Sober, H.A.

7. DEAE-Sephadex chromatography of guanylate oligomers using guanidinium chloride. *Biochim. Biophys. Acta 277 (1972) 290-300,* Olson, A.C., Volkin, E.

8. The synthesis of triaminoacyl-insulins and the use of the t-butyloxy-carbonyl group for the reversible blocking of the amino groups of insulin. *Biochemistry 6 (1967) 3559—3568,* Levy, D., Carpenter, F.H.

9. Ion exchanger from pearl-shaped cellulose gel. *Nature 223 (1969) 499—500,* Determann, H., Meyer, N., Wieland, T.

10. Studies on the chromatography of human serum proteins on diethylaminoethyl (DEAE)-cellulose. I. The effect of the chemical and physical nature of the exchanger. *J. Chromatogr. 15 (1964) 324—335,* James, K., Stanworth, D.R.

11. Gel Filtration in Theory and Practice, Pharmacia LKB Biotechnology AB, S-75182 Uppsala, Sweden.

12. The separation of human globin chains by ion-exchange chromatography on CM-Sepharose CL-6B. *Hemoglobin 3 (1979)13—20,* Sparham, S.J., Huehns, E.R.

13. Agar derivatives for chromatography, electrophoresis and gel-bound enzymes. I. Desulphated and reduced cross-linked agar and agarose in spherical bead form. *J Chromatogr. 60(1971)161—177,* Porath, J., Janson, J.-C., Laas, T.

14. Ion exchange chromatographic characterization of stinging insect vespid venoms. Toxicon (Pergamon Press), 22,1 (1984) 154-160, Einarson, R., Renck, B.

15. Physicochemical considerations in the use of MonoBeads for the separation of Biological Molecules. Protides of the Biological Fluids, 30 (1982) 629-634, Söderberg, L. et al.

16. A simple method for estimating isoelectric points. *Anal. Biochem. 11(1965) 374—*377, Lampson, G.P., Tytell, A.A.

17. Isoelectric points and molecular weights of proteins: a table. J. *Chromatogr.127 (1976)1—28,* Righetti, P.G., Caravaggio, T.

18. Isoelectric points of proteins: a table. *AnaL Biochem. 86 (1978) 620—647,* Malamud, D., Drysdale, J.W.

19. Basic principles used in the selection of MonoBeads ion exchangers for the separation of biopolymers. Protides of the Biological Fluids, 30 (1982) 621-628, Fägerstam, L.G. et al.

20. Use of electrophoretic titration curves for predicting optimal conditions for fast ion exchange chromatography of proteins. *J. Chromatogr. 266 (1983) 409-425,* Haff, L.A., Fägerstam, L.G., Barry, A.R.

21. "Isoelectric Focusing: Principles and Methodes", Technical Booklet Series (1982), Pharmacia Fine Chemicals, Uppsala, Sweden.

22. Interrelationships of human-interferon gamma with lymphotoxin and monocyte cytotoxin. *J. Exp. Med. 159 (1984) 824-843*, Stone-Wolff, D.S., Yip, Y.K., Kelker, H.C. et al.

23. Glass wool as a potential source of artifacts in chromatography. *J. Chromatogr. 152 (1978) 514—516,* Schwartz, D.P.

24. Ion Exchange Chromatography. Protein Purification, Principles, High resolution methods andApplications, Janson, J.C., Ryden, L. (Eds) VCH, Publishers Inc. New York. (1989) 107-148, Karlsson, E., Ryden, L., Brewer, J.

25. Gel Filtration Chromatography. L. Fischer. Elsevier, Amsterdam (1980)

26. Arthropod hemocyanin structure: isolation of eight subunits in the scorpion. *Arch. Biochem. Biophys. 193 (1979)140—149,* Lamy, J., Lamy, J., Weill, J.

27. Rapid isolation of *Escherichia* Coli b-galactosidase by fast protein liquid chromatography. *J. Chromatogr. 393 (1987) 462-465,* Motorin, Y.A. et al.

28. Chromatography of proteins and peptides on Sephadex ion-exchangers: dependence of the resolution on the elution schedule. *FEBS Lett. 14 (1971) 7—10,* Novotny, J.

29. High Performance ion-exchange separation of oxidised and reduced nicotinamide adenine dinucleotides. *Anal. Biochem. 142 (1984) 232-234,* Orr, G.A., Blanchard, J.S.

30. An improved method of gradient elution chromatography and its application to the scparation of urinary ketosteroids. *Arch. Biochem. Biophys. 53 (1954) 258—281,* Lakshmann, T.K., Lieberman, S.

31. A gradient titration apparatus for determining spectrophotometric binding isotherms. *Anal. Biochem.67 (1975) 449—452,* Walz, F. G .

32. FPLC of leukaemia cell N-Acetyl ß-D-Hexosaminidases. *Leukaemia Res.11 (1987) 437-444,* Scott, C.S., Patel, M., Stark, A.N., Roberts, B.E.

33. Presented at Sixth International Congress on Methods in Protein Sequence Analysis, Seattle, Washington, USA. (1986) Bhikhabhai, R., Lindblom, H., Källman, I., Fägarstam, L.

34. Fractionation of DNA restriction fragments with ion exchangers for high performance liquid chromatography. *European Journal of Biochemistry 155 (1986) 203-212,* Müller, W.

35. Inositol triphosphates in carbochal-stimulated rat parotid glands. *Biochem. J., 223 (1984) 237-243,* Irvine, R.F., Letcher, A.J., Lander, D.J., Downes, C.P.;

36. Inositol bis-, tris-, and tetrakis- phosphate(s): Analysis in tissue by HPLC. *Proc. Natl. Acad. Sci. USA., 83 (1986) 4162-4166,* Meek, J.L.

37. Release of intra-cellular Ca^{2+} and elevation of inositol triphosphates by secretagogues in parietal and chief cells isolated from rabbit gastric mucosa. *Biochim. Biophys. Acta., 88 (1986) 116-125,* Chew, C.S., Brown, M.R.

38. Albumin from human plasma: preparation and in vitro properties. in Separation of Plasma proteins. J.M. Curling, ed., Pharmacia Fine Chemicals AB, Uppsala, Sweden. (1983) 51-58. Berglöf, J.H., Eriksson, S., Suomela, H., Curling, J.M.

39. Fast Protein Liquid Chromatography scale-up procedures for the preparation of low molecular weight proteins from urine. *J. Chromatogr. 327 (1985) 269-277,* Cooper, E.H., Turner, R., Webb, J.R., Lindblom, H., Fägerstam, L.

40. FPLC for monitoring microbial and mammalian cell cultures. *Bio/Tecchnology 2 (1984) 777-781,* Frej, A.K. et al.

41. Varietal identification by rapid chromatography (FPLC) of wheat gliadins. 3rd Conference, Royal Australian Institute, Brisbane, Australia. (1983). Batey, I.

42. Rapid extraction and separation of plasma b-endorphin by cation exchange chromatograpy. *J. Chromatogr., 297 (1984) 399-403,* Stenman, U-H., et al.

43. Applications of Fast Protein Liquid Chromatography in the separation of plasma proteins in urine and cerebrospinal fluid. *Clin. Chem., 29 (1983) 1635-1640,* Cooper, E.H. et al.

44. Buffers for pH and metal ion control. Chapman and Hall, Ltd. , London (1974), Perrin, D.D., Dempsey, B.